NEUROSCIENCE RESEARCH PROGRESS

G000021414

GLOBUS PALLIDUS

REGIONAL ANATOMY, FUNCTIONS/DYSFUNCTIONS AND ROLE IN BEHAVIORAL DISORDERS

NEUROSCIENCE RESEARCH PROGRESS

Additional books in this series can be found on Nova's website
under the Series tab.

Additional e-books in this series can be found on Nova's website
under the e-book tab.

NEUROSCIENCE RESEARCH PROGRESS

GLOBUS PALLIDUS

REGIONAL ANATOMY, FUNCTIONS/DYSFUNCTIONS AND ROLE IN BEHAVIORAL DISORDERS

CYNTHIA R. GORDON

AND

THOMAS G. ABBADELLI

EDITORS

New York

Copyright © 2013 by Nova Science Publishers, Inc.

For permission to use material from this book please contact us:
Telephone 631-231-7269; Fax 631-231-8175
Web Site: http://www.novapublishers.com

NOTICE TO THE READER

The Publisher has taken reasonable care in the preparation of this book, but makes no expressed or implied warranty of any kind and assumes no responsibility for any errors or omissions. No liability is assumed for incidental or consequential damages in connection with or arising out of information contained in this book. The Publisher shall not be liable for any special, consequential, or exemplary damages resulting, in whole or in part, from the readers' use of, or reliance upon, this material. Any parts of this book based on government reports are so indicated and copyright is claimed for those parts to the extent applicable to compilations of such works.

Independent verification should be sought for any data, advice or recommendations contained in this book. In addition, no responsibility is assumed by the publisher for any injury and/or damage to persons or property arising from any methods, products, instructions, ideas or otherwise contained in this publication.

This publication is designed to provide accurate and authoritative information with regard to the subject matter covered herein. It is sold with the clear understanding that the Publisher is not engaged in rendering legal or any other professional services. If legal or any other expert assistance is required, the services of a competent person should be sought. FROM A DECLARATION OF PARTICIPANTS JOINTLY ADOPTED BY A COMMITTEE OF THE AMERICAN BAR ASSOCIATION AND A COMMITTEE OF PUBLISHERS.

Additional color graphics may be available in the e-book version of this book.

Library of Congress Cataloging-in-Publication Data

ISBN: 978-1-62948-367-2

Library of Congress Control Number: 2013950577

Published by Nova Science Publishers, Inc. † New York

Contents

Preface

The globus pallidus is a structure in the brain involved in the regulation of voluntary movement. It is part of the basal ganglia, which, among many other things, regulate movements that occur on the subconscious level. In this book, the authors present current research in the study of the regional anatomy, functions/dysfunctions and role in behavioral disorders of the globus pallidus. Topics discussed include imaging of the globus pallidus in patients suffering from pantothenate kinase-associated neurodegeneration (PKAN); anatomo-functional territories and pathophysiological relations in the globus pallidus; a population activity model of cortico-striatal circuitry underlying behavioral inhibition in rats; and the neuropathology of the basal ganglia and its role in the Parkinsonian syndromes with special reference to the globus pallidus.

Chapter 1 - Background and Purpose: PKAN is a rare autosomal recessive disease, typically characterized by dystonia, rigidity and choreoathetosis, and sometimes by cognitive decline. Probably due to a founder effect, PKAN is unusually frequent in the southwest of the Dominican Republic. Although the clinical symptomatology may differ, all Dominican patients show one identical mutation of the PANK2 gene and in most cases, the typical "eye-of-the-tiger" sign in Magnetic Resonance Imaging (MRI). The authors analyzed the changing appearance of this sign in MRI with advancing age as well as other structural and functional aspects which might help to illuminate the clinical expression and progression of the disease.

Patients and Methods: Included are the structural MRI findings of 21 patients and 3 genetically confirmed, but symptom-free cases from the Dominican Republic (age range: 7 to 41 years), 13 gene carriers and 44 controls. MRI was carried out on a 3T scanner and included at least a diffusion-weighted sequence. In most cases, the authors could determine the extent of the abnormal signal loss in T2W as well as calculate T2 time, Fractional Anisotropy (FA) and Mean Diffusivity (MD), grey matter density (Voxel Based Morphometry,VBM) and cerebral activation during rest and hand movement (BOLD contrast). Results were correlated to age and degree of dystonia recorded by the Burke-Fahn-Marsden Scale. In addition, the authors included MRI findings from 9 patients (4 to 76 years) from the USA for qualitative evaluation, but without quantitative assessment.

Results: The first lesion appearing in the younger patients was a bright spot in the anterior part of the globus pallidus, whereas the surrounding signal loss came later and was accompanied by a significant reduction in T2 time. In the anterior part of the internal capsule, FA was reduced and MD increased. From these values, only the extent of the abnormal signal reduction in the globus pallidus correlated significantly with age, but not with the degree of dystonia. VBM revealed a decrease in grey matter volume in the midcingular gyrus, and the same area showed increased functional activity during resting state. In the motor activation study, patients presented a "hyperactivation" of their motor network starting in the ipsilateral cerebellum and proceeding to the contralateral premotor and primary motor cortex, the supplementary motor area and finally to the putamen. These activations showed a positive correlation with the degree of dystonia of the contralateral arm ($p \leq 0.001$).

Discussion: As the primary PKAN lesion, the authors could confirm the appearance of a bright spot in the globus pallidus which underlines the crucial role of the globus pallidus in PKAN dystonia. Iron accumulation starts later in an area below the primary lesion and increases over time. Because it is not significantly correlated to the degree of dystonia, it might not be a useful parameter for disease progression. The further clinical course of the disease might be determined at least partially by secondary functional compensation mechanisms leading to a "hyperactivation" of the motor network and a decreased grey matter volume and increased activity during resting state in the midcingulate gyrus. The clinical significance of the latter two new findings remains to be determined.

Chapter 2 - The very fine somatotopic arrangement of the cortico-basal-ganglia-thalamo-cortical circuit has been extensively detailed in anatomical and physiological studies. Like other basal ganglia, the globus pallidus (GP) maintains three anatomofunctional territories, which are referred to as the sensorimotor territory (for processing sensory and motor information); associative territory (cognitive information); and limbic territory (emotional and motivational information). Thus, movement disorders: dystonia and dyskinesia, cognitive disorders: attention deficit with or without hyperactivity, and stereotyped behaviors can develop because of GP dysfunction. GP dysfunction is crucial to dystonia according to neurophysiological studies, functional imaging data, and animal models. Underactivity of the internal segment of GP - but above all irregularities in pallidal activity – has been emphasized as part of the pathophysiology of idiopathic dystonia, including overall increased direct putaminopallidal activity and reduced subthalamo-internal pallidal input. GP lesions are also associated with behavioral disorders, such as attention deficit hyperactivity disorder or obsessive-compulsive disorder, if damage occurs in the associative and limbic territories respectively. In this chapter, the authors review the findings of several important studies on the effects of GP lesions in animals and humans and discuss the role GP plays in the pathophysiology of dystonia, cognitive, and behavioral disorders.

Chapter 3 - A failure of response inhibition is thought to contribute to several psychological disorders. Response inhibition can be assessed with tasks that require the ability to stop an initiated response, such as the stop signal reaction time task. Numerous studies have shown that the basal ganglia are critical for action selection and motor control. The authors constructed a neural network model that proposes a specific neurobiological mechanism for stop signal reaction time performance, using the known dynamics and interactions of the basal ganglia. There are six groups of nuclei in the authors' model: the cortex, the striatal dopamine D1 receptor expressing neurons, the striatal dopamine D2 receptor expressing neurons, the subthalamic nucleus (STN), the globus pallidus external segment (GPe), and an output population comprised of both the substantia nigra pars reticulata (SNr) and globus pallidus internal segment (GPi). The authors used a stochastic version of a Wilson-Cowan-type system of nonlinear differential equations to depict the spiking and synaptic activity of these neural populations. The firing rate of three different channels within the SNr/GPi neuron population representing three different actions can be monitored to determine if a particular action was selected in the simulation. The authors' model was able to reproduce general phenomena observed in the stop signal reaction time task in previous experiments and behavioral data that the authors collected from a group of rats trained in a stop signal reaction time task. Collectively, these results suggest that a population-level model can be used to understand the contribution of the basal ganglia to action selection.

Chapter 4 - The globus pallidus, together with the striatum (caudate nucleus and putamen), substantia nigra, nucleus accumbens, and subthalamic nucleus constitute the basal ganglia, a group of nuclei which act as a single functional unit. The basal ganglia have extensive connections to the cerebral cortex and thalamus and exert control over a variety of functions including voluntary motor control, procedural learning, and motivation. The action of the globus pallidus is primarily inhibitory and balances the excitatory influence of other areas of the brain such as the cerebral cortex and cerebellum. Neuropathological changes affecting the basal ganglia play a significant role in the clinical signs and symptoms observed in the 'parkinsonian syndromes' viz., Parkinson's disease (PD), progressive supranuclear palsy (PSP), dementia with Lewy bodies (DLB), multiple system atrophy (MSA), and corticobasal degeneration (CBD). There is increasing evidence that different regions of the basal ganglia are differentially affected in these disorders. Hence, in all parkinsonian disorders and especially PD, there is significant pathology affecting the substantia nigra and its dopamine projection to the striatum. However, in PSP and MSA, the globus pallidus is also frequently affected while in DLB and CBD, whereas the caudate nucleus and/or putamen are affected, the globus pallidus is often spared. This chapter reviews the functional pathways of the basal ganglia, with special reference to the globus pallidus, and the role that differential pathology in these regions may play in the movement disorders characteristic of the parkinsonian syndromes.

In: Globus Pallidus   ISBN: 978-1-62948-367-2
Editors: C.R. Gordon, T.G. Abbadelli   © 2013 Nova Science Publishers, Inc.

Chapter 1

Imaging of the Globus Pallidus in Patients Suffering from Pantothenate Kinase-Associated Neurodegeneration (PKAN)

P. Stoeter[1,], P. Roa-Sanchez[2], H. Speckter[1],*
E. Perez-Then[3], C. Vilchez[1], J. Oviedo[1]
and R. Rodriguez-Raecke[4]
[1]Dep. of Radiology
[2]Dep. of Neurology
[3]Dep. of Management of Science, CEDIMAT, Santo Domingo,
Republica Dominicana
[4]Neurological Clinic, Medical School, Hannover, Germany

Abstract

Background and Purpose: PKAN is a rare autosomal recessive disease, typically characterized by dystonia, rigidity and choreoathetosis, and sometimes by cognitive decline. Probably due to a founder effect, PKAN is unusually frequent in the southwest of the Dominican Republic.

* Corresponding author: Peter Stoeter, MD, Dep. de Radiología, CEDIMAT, Plaza de la Salud, Santo Domingo, Republica Dominicana, Tel. 809 565 9989, Cel. 829 343 6544. Email: peter.stoeter@gmx.de.

Although the clinical symptomatology may differ, all Dominican patients show one identical mutation of the PANK2 gene and in most cases, the typical "eye-of-the-tiger" sign in Magnetic Resonance Imaging (MRI). We analyzed the changing appearance of this sign in MRI with advancing age as well as other structural and functional aspects which might help to illuminate the clinical expression and progression of the disease.

Patients and Methods: Included are the structural MRI findings of 21 patients and 3 genetically confirmed, but symptom-free cases from the Dominican Republic (age range: 7 to 41 years), 13 gene carriers and 44 controls. MRI was carried out on a 3T scanner and included at least a diffusion-weighted sequence. In most cases, we could determine the extent of the abnormal signal loss in T2W as well as calculate T2 time, Fractional Anisotropy (FA) and Mean Diffusivity (MD), grey matter density (Voxel Based Morphometry,VBM) and cerebral activation during rest and hand movement (BOLD contrast). Results were correlated to age and degree of dystonia recorded by the Burke-Fahn-Marsden Scale. In addition, we included MRI findings from 9 patients (4 to 76 years) from the USA for qualitative evaluation, but without quantitative assessment.

Results: The first lesion appearing in the younger patients was a bright spot in the anterior part of the globus pallidus, whereas the surrounding signal loss came later and was accompanied by a significant reduction in T2 time. In the anterior part of the internal capsule, FA was reduced and MD increased. From these values, only the extent of the abnormal signal reduction in the globus pallidus correlated significantly with age, but not with the degree of dystonia. VBM revealed a decrease in grey matter volume in the midcingular gyrus, and the same area showed increased functional activity during resting state. In the motor activation study, patients presented a "hyperactivation" of their motor network starting in the ipsilateral cerebellum and proceeding to the contralateral premotor and primary motor cortex, the supplementary motor area and finally to the putamen. These activations showed a positive correlation with the degree of dystonia of the contralateral arm ($p \leq 0.001$).

Discussion: As the primary PKAN lesion, we could confirm the appearance of a bright spot in the globus pallidus which underlines the crucial role of the globus pallidus in PKAN dystonia. Iron accumulation starts later in an area below the primary lesion and increases over time. Because it is not significantly correlated to the degree of dystonia, it might not be a useful parameter for disease progression. The further clinical course of the disease might be determined at least partially by secondary functional compensation mechanisms leading to a "hyperactivation" of the motor network and a decreased grey matter volume and increased activity during resting state in the midcingulate gyrus. The clinical significance of the latter two new findings remains to be determined.

Introduction

Pantothenate Kinase Associated Neurodegeneration (PKAN) is the most frequent entity among the various forms of diseases grouped under the term of Neurodegeneration with Brain Iron Accumulation (NBIA), formerly known as Hallervorden-Spatz disease [1]. This genetically heterogenous group of conditions is characterized by abnormal and progressive accumulation of iron in the basal ganglia. In addition and as already described in the initial report [2], "spheroid bodies" can be found in histological samples. The histological changes mainly affect the globus pallidus, but may extent into the medial putamen and internal capsule, the subthalamic nucleus and parts of the substantia nigra.

PKAN is an autosomal-recessive disorder. With an estimated prevalence of 1:1,000,000, it belongs to the "Rare Diseases" [3]. Over one decade ago, the responsible mutation has been localized to the PANK2 gene on the chromosomal position 20p13. Most mutations are missense and have been detected in all 7 exons of PANK2, but deletions, duplications and splice-site mutations have been reported as well [4]. The resulting metabolic defect affects the formation of one of the four different varieties of pantothenate kinase. These enzymes are regulating the production of coenzyme A from vitamin B5 and thus are involved in energy metabolism and pathways requiring participation of coenzyme A as for bile acid conjugation and lipid metabolism [5-8].

In PKAN, pathological changes appear to be limited to the globus pallidus with variable involvement of neighbouring parts of the basal ganglia, whereas the cortex, most parts of the brain stem and the rest of the central grey matter is not affected. Iron has mainly been shown in a mainly perivascular distribution. There are some iron-loaded astrocytes and macrophages, but generally, inflammatory response is unremarkable. The "spheroids" are described as roundish, slightly granular or homogenous structures up to 100 μm in diameter representing dystrophic and degenerating neurons. Tau expression is faint, without neurofibrillary tangles [9].

Clinically, PKAN belongs to the group of secondary dystonias. In the "classical" form, the onset of symptoms is early in childhood and has a progressive course. In about one quarter of cases however, the disease starts atypically late during the teenage years or early adulthood, followed by slower progression, and there are intermediate courses. The clinical manifestation is variable and mainly characterized by dystonic movements affecting the oro-pharyngeal or cervical area, the trunk or extremities. Gait or postural difficulties leading to frequent falls are initial symptoms, accompanied by signs of paramidal tract involvement as spasticity, hyperreflexia and Babinski's sign. Oculomotor abnormalities suggestive of midbrain involvement are common. Parkinsonian features have been described in older patients as well as cognitive decline, impulsive behavior and pigmentary retinopathy [10, 11]. Death usually occurs 10 years after the onset, but the course may be more prolonged [12].

In Magnetic Resonance Imaging (MRI), the "eye-of-the-tiger"-sign is regarded as the classical finding indicating the presence of PKAN [13-15]. In T2- and T2 star weighted imaging, it consists of a bright spot in the antero-medial part of the globus pallidus surrounded by a dark area covering the posterior parts of this nucleus. Although not being 100% pathognomonic [16], this well-characterized MR finding is regarded to enable a specific diagnosis and to differentiate PKAN from other varieties of NBIA. However, the absolute correlation of this sign and PKAN, which means that all patients showing the PANK2 gene mutation also show the "tiger's eye" and vice versa, has been questioned by others suggesting that its appearance may change over time with increasing accumulation of iron which is responsible for the signal drop in the globus pallidus outside the "eye" itself [17, 18]. However, in spite of a great number of case reports and more extensive group studies, not all aspects of the "Eye-of-the Tiger" sign have been described in detail, mainly its different appearance in T1-weighted scans as well as in diffusion- and susceptibility weighted imaging.

In contrast to other varieties of NBIA, severe abnormalities of grey and white matter outside the basal ganglia have not been reported in routine MR imaging of patients with a PANK2 mutation with the exception of "mild cerebellar or cerebral atrophy" in some cases [13] and "hypointensities" of the substantia nigra in four and the dentate nucleus in one out of five cases [19]. From the so-called "advanced" MRI methods, Diffusion Tensor Imaging has been applied showing an increase of Fractional Anisotropy in the globus pallidus [20] in PKAN patients and their non-affected siblings [21]. In contrast to other forms of dystonia, where some increase of grey matter areas has been reported [22], quantitative grey matter analysis has not been carried out elsewhere.

Several MR studies of cerebral activation have been carried out in generalized dystonia [23, 24] and the following patho-physiological network model has been proposed: a hyperactivation of the motor system due to a reduced feed-back inhibition [25, 26], a senso-motor dysbalance [27] and a generalized hyper-plasticity with a reduced capability to maintain homeostasis

[28]. In primary torsion dystonia which resembles the clinical picture of PKAN, the results of structural and functional PET and MR studies are consistent with the view of primary torsion dystonia as a neuro-developmental circuit disorder involving cortico-striatal-pallido-thalamo-cortical and related cerebello-thalamo-cortical pathways [29]. Some of these changes are thought to be more related to genetic conditions whereas others could represent adaptive responses. To our knowledge, there are no similar reports from patients with PKAN dystonia carried out by other groups in the literature.

The present study, parts of which have been reported elsewhere [16, 30-32], is based on a relatively large and homogenous group of genetically identical PKAN patients and preclinical cases from the Dominican Republic and additional scans of PKAN patients from the USA. It is aimed to look more into details of the presentation of the "eye-of-the-tiger" sign in different MRI sequences and into its development over time in order to possibly find some sort of imaging indicator for the progression of the disease. In addition, we will describe the results of advanced structural imaging of the grey and white matter and combine these findings with those of a motor activation and a default mode network study which we were able to carry out in some of our patients. The final goal of this synthesis of imaging findings is to get insight into the role of the globus pallidus in the pathophysiology underlying the dystonic movements in PKAN.

Patients and Methods

Patients, Family Members and Volunteers

We analyzed the imaging data from a group of 21 patients living in the south-west of the Dominican Republic or with family roots to this region, all suffering from PKAN due to an identical missense mutation of the PANK2 gene (c.680 A>G, p.Y227C). Probably due to a founder effect in a rather closed area without much migration of the population, the disease shows an extremely high prevalence mainly around the small town of Cabral with more than 1 case per 10,000 inhabitants. Patients were between 10 – 41 years old, 13 females and 8 males. All patients received a detailed neurologic examination including video and clinical scaling. In this group, we also included the MRI data of three additional young and still "preclinical" family members with the same homozygous mutation, but at the time of scanning still without clinical manifestation (7, 10 and 11 years old, 2 females and 1 male).

From these individuals, all clinical data, mainly their dystonia score according to the Burke-Fahn-Marsden Scale, were available.

In order to increase the age range of patients for documentation of basic changes in the basal ganglia, we also included 9 routine MR scans from genetically confirmed PKAN patients from the USA between 4 –and 76 years of age without knowledge of their clinical findings. Their data however were not used for quantitative evaluation.

In addition, we analyzed the MRI data from a group of 16 family members of the patients from the Dominican Republic. 13 of them were heterogenous gene carriers suffering from the same mutation (10 – 67 years of age, 7 women and 6 men). The family members had been checked clinically for absence of obvious clinical signs of dystonia. For comparison, we used the MRI results of 44 healthy volunteers from the region of Santo Domingo (8-41 years of age, 26 females and 18 males) without any relations to the patients, their families or the special region in the south-west of the Dominican Republic described above.

In most cases, the scanning procedure could be performed without anesthesia, but in 6 patients, mild sedation had to be applied. All parts of the present project had been approved by the local ethic committee, and informed consent had been received by every participant in the study.

Acquisition of MRI Data

Type of Scanner

All examinations in the Dominican Republic were performed on the same 3 Tesla scanner (Achieva, Philips/Netherlands, Release 2.6), using an 8 channel SENSE receiver head coil. Patients in the USA were examined on different equipment, with magnetic fields of 1.5 Tesla in 8 patients and of 3 Tesla in one patient. In the following, only the parameters of sequences used on the Achieva 3 Tesla scanner are indicated:

Basic Structural and Diffusion Weighted Sequences

T2-weighted sequence: TR/TE=2050/80 ms, 25 transversal slices, thickness 5 mm, matrix 512x512. This sequence was applied to all patients included in the study.

T2 star weighted sequence: TR/TE=592/16 ms, 28 transversal slices, thickness 4 mm, matrix 512x512. This sequence was applied to 21 patients/"preclinical"cases.

T1-weighted sequence: 3-dimensional Turbo Field Echo sequence, TR/TE=6.73/3.11 ms, 180 sagittal slices, voxel size 1 mm³. This sequence was applied to 23 patients/"preclinical" cases.

Diffusion weighted sequence: Spin echo based sequence, TR/TE=2508/65 ms, 24 transversal slices, thickness 4 mm and gap 1.5 mm, acquisition matrix 128x128. This sequence was applied to 21 patients/"preclinical"cases.

Susceptibility weighted sequence: 3 dimensional multi-shot gradient echo EPI-based sequence "VenBold" with TR/TE of 16/23 ms, flip angle 10°, acquisition matrix 220/182 and measured voxel size of 1x0.5x0.5 mm. The sequence was applied in 12 patients and 1 "preclinical" case from the Dominican Republic and mainly used to evaluate involvement of nuclei below the globus pallidus.

Evaluation of these scans was performed in a qualitative way by two experienced neuroradiologists looking for abnormalities of shape and contrast of cerebral grey and white matter and enlargement of cerebro-spinal fluid spaces. The examiners were not aware of the clinical status. However, due to the presence of the "Eye-of-the-Tiger" sign, a completely blinded evaluation of the scans was not possible.

In addition, we looked for a way to quantify the extension of the abnormally dark area of the globus pallidus on T2-weighted scans as these scans are usually available in routine MRI. For this purpose, we measured the mean signal and the standard deviation in a Region of Interest (ROI) laid into the anterior part of the corpus callosum and masked all pixels above the mean value minus 5 standard deviations. By this procedure, all voxels related to grey and white matter could be excluded with the exception of voxels of abnormally low signal within the globus pallidus. The area of the "surviving" pixels was measured on each cut and, divided by the intracranial area of the same cut, served as a relative measure of the extension of abnormal signal reduction within the globus pallidus. The resulting data were checked for dependence on magnetic field strength by comparing the results from 1.5 and 3 Tesla field scanners using a 2-armed t-test.

Measurements of T2 Time and T2 Star Time

These examinations were performed in order to determine a surrogate parameter for the accumulation of iron. Measurements of T2 time were carried out in 2 ways: First, 17 patients and one "preclinical" case as well as 13 carriers and 14 volunteers were scanned using 1 transversal slice of 5mm thickness, matrix 256x256 through the globus pallidus measured with 8 different TEs (20 – 160 ms) and TR=2000 ms.

To include the red nucleus and substantia nigra, we acquired a second coronal scan in 6 patients, 2 preclinical cases and 19 volunteers, positioned through the basal ganglia and midbrain: 3D-Turbo Spin Echo sequence of 5 slices à 4 mm, 32 echoes beginning at a TE=7.6 ms and a TE spacing of 8.1 ms, TR 509 ms, FOV 230 mm, measured voxel size 1 mm, reconstruction matrix 240x240.

Measurement of T2 star time was performed on coronal scans only in 6 patients, 2 preclinical cases and 19 volunteers, using the same position as described above: 3 dimensional Fast Field Echo sequence, 10 slices à 4 mm, 10 echoes beginning at TE=2.1 ms and a spacing of TE of 3.2 ms, TR 329 ms, FOV 230mm, measured voxel size 1.3mm, reconstruction matrix 240x240.

Although both sequences used in the coronal plane had been optimized specially for short scanning time, most patients did not tolerate these additional measurements without giving rise to severe movement artifacts.

T2 and T2 star time maps were automatically calculated by the scanner software which uses an algorithm based on Maximum Likelihood Estimation [33]. From these maps, T2 and T2 star time values were taken from ROIs placed individually and free-hand into the globus pallidus (sparing the bright spot of the "tiger's eye"), thalamus, substantia nigra and red nucleus and –if present- the hyperintensity in the anterior part of the globus pallidus (the "tiger's eye") of both sides.

Diffusion Tensor Imaging (DTI)

We performed DTI (as well as spectroscopy) mainly to look for white matter changes not visible in the basic images. DTI was carried out in 21 patients and one preclinical case, 13 carriers and 27 volunteers, using b-values of 0 s/mm^2 and of 800 s/mm^2 and gradients applied in 32 directions as well as TR/TE=5888/60 ms, slice thickness 2 mm and a matrix of 128x128. For calculation of Mean Diffusivity (MD) maps, Fractional Anisotropy (FA) maps and tensors, we used home-made software [34]. These parameters were determined in the white matter as well as in the basal ganglia and thalamus. For evaluation of white matter structures, we placed ROIs of a size of 9.7 mm^2 using the program Image J (http://rsb.info.nih.gov/ij) into the FA and MD maps with support from colour maps for tract identification. In detail, ROIs were placed bilaterally into the fronto-basal, mid-frontal and occipital white matter, the cerebral peduncles, the anterior and the posterior parts of the internal capsule, the cingulum and the central cortico-spinal tracts at the level of the cingulum. For determination of DTI parameters from the basal ganglia and thalamus, individual ROIs were drawn on the b0-maps and then transferred to the MD and FA maps. In the presence of an "eye-of-the-tiger" sign, this area was evaluated separately and not included in the ROI of the hypointense part of the globus pallidus. Reproducibility of this method of DTI parameter measurement by placement of ROIs has been previously shown to be sufficiently high [35].

Spectroscopy

1H single voxel spectroscopy was applied to 18 patients and 13 carriers. Using a STEAM sequence (TE=35ms) and scanner-provided software, N-Acetyl-Aspartate (NAA), Choline (Cho) and Creatine (Cre) peaks were measured from 2x2x2 cm voxels placed into the parieto-occipital white matter of one hemisphere. For further evaluation, we determined the relations of NAA/Cre and Cho/Cre.

Volumetry of Grey Matter

Volume changes of grey matter structures were assessed by Voxel-Based Morphometry (VBM) in 12 adult patients (mean age 27, range 18 to 41, 8 female) and an age- and gender-matched group of non-affected volunteers (mean age 26, range 18 to 41, 8 female). One patient had to be excluded from the original cohort of affected individuals scanned with the 3 dimensional T1 weighted sequence as described above because of movement artefacts not allowing for quantitative analysis. Grey matter density was calculated using VBM 8. This program is based on high resolution structural 3D MR images and allows for applying voxel-wise statistics to detect regional differences in gray matter density or volumes. In summary, pre-processing involved spatial normalization, gray matter segmentation, non-linear modulation and smoothing with a kernel of 10x10x10 mm. The resulting volumes were analysed with a two-sample t-test. Significance was assumed in case of $p \leq 0.001$ analysing the whole brain.

Functional Imaging of the Resting State

Included were 4 patients, one "preclinical" case (mean age: 14.4 years) and a control group of 9 healthy volunteers (mean age: 21.6 years). Imaging was performed with an Echo-Planar-Imaging (EPI) based gradient echo sequence of TR=2000 ms, 34 slices of 3 mm thickness and a gap of 0.75 mm covering the whole head, Field of View (FOV) of 192 mm and a voxel size of 2.4x2.4x3 mm. During 10 minutes, 300 dynamics were acquired. Subjects lying in the scanner were instructed to stay quietly with eyes closed, not thinking of special issues. Image preprocessing and statistical analysis were performed with Statistical Parametric Mapping (SPM8, www.fil.ion.ucl .ac.uk/spm) running under Matlab (MathWorks). Prepro-cessing steps consisted out of slice timing, realignment, spatial normalization to a standard EPI template and smoothing with an 8 mm Gaussian kernel. Independent Component Analysis was performed by GroupICATv2.0 Globus Pallidus: Regional Anatomy, Functions/Dysfunctions and Role in Behavioral Disorders sourceforge.net) using Infomax algorithm. 2 components were correlated to the degree of dystonia (Burke-Fahn-Marsden scale) using SPM 2nd level multiple regression analysis. For setting up the multiple regression model, the correlating Burke-Fahn-Marsden-scale was used as a parametric regressor, implementing different weights of values from imaging data, depending on the single persons' severity of dystonia. That component which showed the cluster with the highest level of correlation to the dystonia scale was analyzed further for group comparison between patients and volunteers in a t-test model. Because of the difference of age between the group of patients and volunteers, two evaluations were performed, one including all patients and volunteers, and a second one with age-matched pairs. Finally, to correct for multiple comparisons, we applied Family-Wise Error (FWE) correction which is implemented in SPM for group comparison and regression analysis.

Functional Imaging of Motor Activation

So-called "functional" MRIs of motor activation were carried out in 6 patients and 1 "preclinical" case and an age-matched group of non-affected volunteers. FMRI was performed in a similar way as described above using the same EPI-based gradient echo sequence (TR 2 s, 34 slices, voxel size 2.4x2.4x3 mm) over 10 min. During this time, 300 dynamics were acquired. We used an event-related motor activation paradigm: subjects lying in thescanner were requested to shortly press the pneumatic ball of an acoustic alarm system with their right hand in response to a visual cue in approximate intervals of 15 s. One severely affected patient had to use his less impaired left hand and his fMRI data were flipped, targeting the motor cortex. The induced noise was recorded on a PC sound track and converted into a time line of events. Image preprocessing and statistical analysis were performed with Statistical Parametric Mapping (SPM8, www.fil.ion.ucl.ac.uk/spm) running under Matlab (MathWorks). Preprocessing steps consisted out of slice timing, realignment, spatial normalization to a standard EPI template and smoothing with an 8 mm Gaussian kernel.

The recorded time line indicated the "onset" of responses in the SPM matrix at the moment of muscle contraction at the time point of 0 s. By subtraction of 1 and 2 s from this time line, we were able to model the time course of preceding cerebral activations. For data analysis the approach of the general linear model was used, modeling the event "motor response" in a first level matrix for each subject. For every time line (0 s, -1 s, -2 s) a new first level matrix was estimated to prevent correlation of the regressors. Coefficients for all regressors were estimated with the approach of least squares, effects were tested with appropriate linear contrasts of the parameter estimates for the hemodynamic response function regressor, resulting in a t-value for each voxel. The main effect of "motor response" from the first level analysis was used in a second level matrix to contrast groups in a paired t-test model, and a multiple regression model with the Burke-Fahn-Marsden-scale as predictor, setting the threshold for significance to $p < 0.01$ for group comparison and to $p < 0.001$ for correlation analysis, because in this special case of rare disease we have to deal with small effects in the group analysis for we can only investigate a few subjects. Nevertheless, FWE correction was applied as well.

Results

Qualitative Evaluation of T2-, T2 star-, T1- and Diffusion Weighted Images

To assess the changing appearance of the "Eye-of-the-Tiger" sign in the globus pallidus over time, we compared the 4 cases below the age of ten (three from the USA and one from the Dominican Republic) with the majority of cases between 10 and 30 years of age and those 5 cases above the age of 30 (one from the USA and four from the Dominican Republic).

Below 10 Years Old

In the youngest one, a 4 year old symptomatic boy, all sequences (including diffusion-weightening, but with the exception of T1) showed the typical hyperintense area in the antero-medial part of the globus pallidus, and only in T2 star weighted images, an additional tiny dark area was visible inferior to the bright spot (Figure 1).

The hyperintensity in diffusion-weighted imaging was regarded as being related to the high signal measured by the T2-effect included in each diffusion-weighted sequence in the sense of a "shine-through", because there was no corresponding signal drop in the calculated Apparent Diffusion Coefficient (ADC) map.

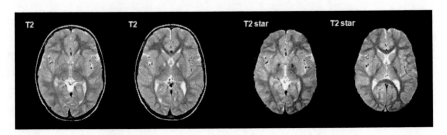

Figure 1. 4-year-old male symptomatic patient. Transversal T2 and T2 star weighted sections show circumscribed hyperintensity at the level of the foramen of Monro and just a tiny area of signal reduction just below this level (in T2 star images only).

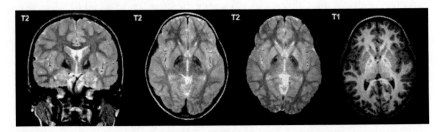

Figure 2. 7-year-old female with genetically homozygous PANK2 mutation, but without clinical symptoms. Fully developed "Eye-of-the-Tiger" sign in T2 weighted images (coronal and transversal), but moderate signal reduction in the area of the "Eye" and slight increase in signal in the rest of the globus pallidus in T1 weighted image (transversal).

A similar aspect of a hyperintensity in T2 imaging, combined with a smaller and lower-situated hypointensity in T2 star weighted imaging, was seen in a symptomatic 6-year-old boy. But in this case, the posterior part of the globus pallidus appeared slightly darker than the surrounding white matter in diffusion weighted imaging. Again, there was no indication of a reduced diffusion in the ADC map in an area corresponding to the bright spot.

A 7-year-old girl from the Dominican Republic however, although still without clinical manifestation, showed a fully developed "Eye-of-the-Tiger" sign in all sequences (Figure 2) with an extension of the hypointensity of the globus pallidus down into the nucleus subthalamicus which had not been involved in the afore-mentioned two cases.

The same applied to a 9-year-old symptomatic girl. In this case, the ADC-map presented slightly increased diffusion values in the center of the globus pallidus surrounded by an inhomogeneous dark rim, which by its arrangement, gave the impression of artifacts possibly caused by local disturbances of the magnetic field.

In T1 weighted images of the group below ten years of age, the globus pallidus appeared iso- to moderately hyperintense. However, the area of the "eye" itself at the level of the Monro's foramen being hyperintense in T2- and diffusion weighted images, showed a slight reduction of signal, but there was no further signal reduction in T1 weighted images inferior the "Eye" and below the level of the foramen of Monro, which might have corresponded to the dark area seen in T2 star weighted images.

10 to 30 Years Old

In T2- and T2 star weighted imaging, most patients of this age showed the classic "Eye-of-the-Tiger" sign consisting of a bright spot in the antero-medial part of the globus pallidus surrounded by a dark area covering the posterior parts of the nucleus. In most patients, the hypointensities were distributed rather inhomogenously within the globus pallidus and could extend into the medial part of the internal capsule. The anterior commissure however, was usually spared and visible as a bundle being isointense to the surrounding brain tissue.

In six patients however, who were between 16 and 30 years old and all from the Dominican Republic, a hyperintense area was not clearly visible in their T2- and T2*-weighted images, all acquired at a magnetic field of 3 Tesla. As reported previously (12), we got the impression that at least in two of them, the "Eye" could have been masked by some central hypointense material surrounded by a moderately bright rim. There was no statistically significant correlation of the presence or absence of a fully developed "Eye-of-the-Tiger" sign to clinical findings (see below).

As in the youngest group, T1 weighted images mainly showed a rather homogeneous and slightly elevated signal in most parts of the globus pallidus except from the area of the "Eye" which presented as a moderate and confined hipointensity. In one 11 year old patient however, who was scanned in a 1.5 Tesla magnetic field, the area of the "Eye" appeared bright also on T1 weighted images.

In addition, 8 of those 14 cases having been scanned in magnetic fields of 3 Tesla, showed severe and circumscribed areas of signal drop just inferior to the "Eye" in a plane slightly above the anterior commissure, but clearly below that of the foramen of Monro (Figure 3). In T1 weighted images which were acquired at magnetic fields of 1.5 Tesla, we did not see these circumscribed areas of severe signal loss.

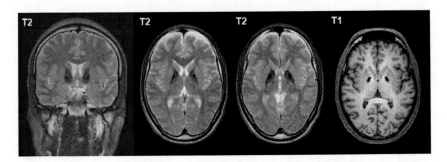

Figure 3. 28-year-old male, symptomatic since 17 years. Severe signal reduction in T2 weighted images (coronal and transversal) in the globus pallidus except from a tiny hyperintensity at the level of the foramen of Monro. Severe and circumscribed signal loss below this level also in T1 weighted image (transversal).

The different location of the "Eye" being hyperintense in T2 weighted images and of the severe signal drop in T1 weighted images could be demonstrated well by applying the masking technique described above to the coronal images used for T2 time calculation. In this series, images of a predominant T1 and of a predominant T2 weightening are acquired in the same measurement. If the hypointense areas in the globus pallidus were defined on the T2 time map as a ROI by masking all pixels with intensities above the mean intensity of the corpus callosum minus 5 standard deviations, this ROI could be overprojected on the T1 weighted images. There, the ROIs of severe hypointensity in T2 weighted images correspond to the areas of varying signal intensity loss whereas the area of the "tiger's eye", which is suppressed by the masking procedure is represented by a moderate signal reduction in T1 weightening and situated well above the region of severe signal reduction. Setting the above-mentioned mask to even lower values, the ROI now represents the areas of highest T2 time reduction and projects mainly on the area of severe signal drop in T1 weightening. There was no significant correlation of these dark areas with the age of patients (Spearman's ρ= 0.322) or with their grade of dystonia (Spearman's ρ= 0.243).

Above 30 Years

Three of the five oldest patients of our group showed an important signal reduction in the globus pallidus in T2- and T2 star weighted images and a rather small bright spot which contained central stripes of reduced signal in three cases. One 32-year-old male and the oldest patient however, a 76-year-old lady did not show any obscuration of the "eye" in T2 weightening.

Table 1. Findings in T2-weighted imaging and correlation to age and dystonia score (Spearman's rank correlation coefficient ρ)

Finding on T2-weighted images	Age		Dystonia score	
	n	mean, range	n	mean, range
Hyperintensity only	2	5 (4, 6)	0	-
Typical "eye-of-the-tiger"-sign	25	16.3 (7-76)	18	21.2 (0-45)
Hypointensity only	6	23.3 (16-30)	6	21.4 (17-29)
Correlation (Spearman's ρ)	ρ = 0.616, p < 0.01		ρ = 0.255, p > 0.05	

Table 2. Relative size of areas of globus pallidus with abnormally reduced signal as measured in 1.5 and 3 Tesla magnetic fields and correlation to age and dystonia score (Spearman's rank correlation coefficient ρ)

	1.5 Tesla scanner		3 Tesla scanner		
	Hypointense area (n=8)	Corr. to age (n=8)	Hypointense area (n=24)	Corr. to age (n=24)	Corr. to dystonia score (n=23)
Left globus pallidus	0.15 %	ρ = 0.258, p > 0.05	1.09 %	ρ = 0.715, p < 0.01	ρ = 0.316, p > 0.05
Right globus pallidus	0.13 %	ρ = 0.213, p > 0.05	1.17 %	ρ = 0.704, p < 0.01	ρ = 0.323, p > 0.05

In two of these patients from the oldest age group, the eye appeared bright on T1 weighted images, similar to the finding in one boy of 11 years described above. One of these cases was examined in a magnetic field of 3 Tesla and the other one in a field of 1.5 Tesla. In one of them, we could determine the T2 time of the area of the "Eye". Its value of 47 ms was below the mean value of this area (53 ms), but well above the minimal value of 39 ms measured in the "Eye" area of our series. Otherwise, the T1 weighted images did not differ from those of the younger groups.

To test for a progression of the obscuration of the "Eye-of-the-Tiger" sign with increasing age and degree of dystonia, we ranked our findings on T2-weighted images in the order "bright spot only", "bright spot and obscuration" and "obscuration only" and found a significant correlation as determined by Spearman's rank correlation coefficient to age (p<0.01), but not to the degree of dystonia (Table 1).

Involvement of Nuclei below the Globus Pallidus

The involvement of nuclei other than the globus pallidus in abnormal signal reduction was juged by inspection of T2*- and –if available- also on susceptibility-weighted images. We did not see any obvious signal reduction of the dentate nucleus and an involvement of the red nucleus in 2 patients only, whereas the subthalamic nucleus was nearly always affected, including the three "preclinical" cases. Only the 2 youngest patients, 4 and 6 years old, and one 10-year-old male, although being symptomatic, did not show any abnormal hypointensity below the globus pallidus.

According to inspection of transversal cuts, the reticular part of the substantia nigra appeared to be involved in 21 patients and one "preclinical" case. However, we did not feel confident about the reliability to distinguish this nucleus from the subthalamic nucleus in this projection. But even on simultaneous transversal, coronal and sagittal reconstructions from our 14 susceptibility weighted data sets, where the topographic differentiation of these two areas is possible, the characterization of a signal reduction as "abnormal", turned out to be possible with some confidence in one patient only.

Quantitative Evaluation of T2-Weighted Images

Further quantitative evaluation was aimed to assess the area of abnormal signal reduction (5 SDs below the mean signal of the anterior part of the corpus callosum in T2-weighted imaging, as described in "Methods"). To correlate the extension of the abnormally hypointense areas with age, we had to divide the cases in 2 groups according to the field strength applied during MRI. An evaluation of the group as a whole was not possible because the amount of signal reduction strongly depended on the magnitude of the magnetic field. The comparison of 6 age-matched patients showed a five times larger average extension of the relative area of signal reduction (0.14 % vs. 0.76 %) in images acquired at 3 Tesla, which was highly significant ($p < 0.0001$, 2-armed t-test).

Calculation of Spearman's rank correlation coefficient showed a significant correlation between age and extension of the abnormal obscuration for the 24 patients scanned at 3 Tesla for the left and for the right globus pallidus ($p < 0.01$), but no significant correlation for the 8 patients scanned at 1.5 Tesla (Table 2). However, the correlation between the relative area of hypointensity and the degree of dystonia according to the Burke-Fahn-Marsden Scale, which could be calculated only for the 23 cases from the Dominican Republic scanned at 3 Tesla, was not significant.

Measurement of T2- and T2 Star Time

Measurement of T2 time and T2 star time from coronal time maps supported the impression of the qualitative assessment: there was a highly significant time reduction in the globus pallidus ($p<0.01$ for both values, patients vs. volunteers), whereas in the substantia nigra, the reduction of T2 time and T2 star time just reached the level of significance ($p \leq 0.05$, Table 3). The T2 time and T2 star time of the red nucleus didn't show significant differences between patients and volunteers.

The T2 and T2 star times of the two "preclinical cases" were in between those from the patients and the volunteers (globus pallidus: 34.9 ms and 13.2 ms) or even higher (substantia nigra: 51.3 ms and 34.0 ms, and red nucleus: 58.9 ms and 43.1 ms).

The T2 time values, which were calculated from one transversal slice, differed considerably from those calculated from coronal slices (30.6 ms for the right and 30.0 ms for the left globus pallidus vs. 23.7 ms and 22.0 ms) for patients, but not for volunteers.

Table 3. T2- time and T2 star time of globus pallidus, substancia nigra and red nucleus (in ms) from coronal slices

	Patients	Volunteers		Patients	Volunteers	
	Globus pallidus right			Globus pallidus left		
T2 time	23.73±1.92	44.60±2.08	P< 0.01*	22.02±2.08	43.33±4.12	P< 0.01*
T2 star time	7.60±1.66	27.25±2.18	P< 0.01*	7.18± 2.41	27.94± 2.35	P< 0.01*

	Substantia nigra right			Substantia nigra left		
T2 time	40.48±4.55	45.95±4.53	P<0.025*	41.30± 4.04	46.27± 4.96	P< 0.05*
T2 star time	22.96±3.12	27.33±3.01	P< 0.01*	22.42± 3.20	27.45± 3.46	P< 0.01*

	Nucleus ruber right			Nucleus ruber left		
T2 time	52.45±4.00	48.68±3.88	P> 0.05	52.98±4.00	48.72±3.85	P> 0.05
T2 star time	39.36±7.77	35.19±4.23	P> 0.05	38.24±7.02	34.81± 4.07	P> 0.05

*) significant difference (patients vs. volunteers) according to Mann-Whitney U test.

This finding corresponds to the fact that the loss of signal seen in these images starts in and mainly affects the anterior part of the globus pallidus, which was completely included in the ROI drawn for measurements in the coronal T2 time maps, but only partly included in the ROI drawn on transversal T2 time maps.

Nevertheless, the differences between patients and volunteers as well as between patients and carriers were significant ($p<0.01$), whereas we saw no significant difference between carriers and volunteers.

Table 4. Fractional anisotropy (FA, units x10^{-3}) and Mean Diffusivity (MD, 10^{-6} mm²/s) of globus pallidus and thalamus in patients (1 "preclinical" case included), carriers and volunteers

	FA globus pallidus		MD globus pallidus		FA thalamus		MD thalamus	
	R	L	R	L	R	L	R	L
Patients Mean ± SD	437.2 ± 69.3	484.9 ± 81.6	848.4 ± 132.0	786.5 ± 123.3	319.4 ± 41.9	334.2 ± 45.2	741.4 ± 40.6	732.8 ± 30.1
Carriers Mean ± SD	361.5 ± 64.3	387.4 ± 75.5	800.7 ± 95.6	726.6 ± 122.9	383.3 ± 69.2	362.4 ± 35.3	754.9 ± 42.2	743.9 ± 37.8
Volunteers Mean ± SD	367.3 ± 36.7	379.7 ± 53.8	792.6 ± 44.5	709.8 ± 43.7	364.3 ± 49.6	365.8 ± 55.6	761.8 ± 52.6	740.1 ± 51.8
Pat. vs. Car.	P<0.0001*	P=0.001*	p>0.05	p=0.008*	p=0.008*	p>0.05	p>0.05	p>0.05
Pat. vs. Vol.	p=0.0001*	P<0.0001*	p>0.05	p>0.05	p=0.0007*	p=0.018*	p>0.05	p>0.05
Car. vs. Vol.	p>0.05	p>0.05	p>0.05	p>0.05	p>0.05	p>0.05	p>0.05	p>0.05

*) significant difference according to t-test.

Parameters of Diffusion Tensor Imaging

FA of the globus pallidus was found to be elevated significantly on both sides, with a high level of significance as compared to volunteers, and to a slightly lesser degree in comparison to carriers. This increase of FA was accompanied by a not expected, however insignificant elevation of MD (Table 4). Within the "Tiger's Eye" area, FA was importantly reduced to values of 0.268 units on the right and to 0,256 units on the left side.

This reduction was not only remarkable in comparison to the surrounding globus pallidus of patients, but also in comparison to values of the surrounding basal ganglia of control subjects. MD of this area was strongly elevated (978x10^{-6} mm²/s on the right and 1021x10^{-6} mm²/s on the left side). Both values from the "Tiger's Eye" area, FA and MD, were the lowest resp. highest ones measured in this study. The thalamus of patients showed a significant reduction of FA ($p \leq 0.018$, vs. volunteers) on both sides without accompanying alterations of MD.

Table 5. Fractional anisotropy (FA, units x10^{-3}) and Mean Diffusivity (MD, 10^{-6} mm²/s) of pedunculus cerebri and anterior part of internal capsule in patients (1 "preclinical" case included), carriers and volunteers

	FA pedunculus cer.		MD pedunculus cer.		FA ant. capsula int.		MD ant. capsula int.	
	R	L	R	L	R	L	R	L
Patients Mean ± SD	812.1 ± 56.0	824.8 ± 56.8	790.4 ± 96.6	772.9 ± 81	562.6 ± 73.9	566.1 ± 78.5	795.5 ± 57.7	774.5 ± 52.8
Carriers Mean ± SD	801.2 ± 42.5	812.6 ± 48.5	743.1 ± 46.4	730.4 ± 33.7	743.5 ± 83.3	806.2 ± 53.1	789.9 ± 70.5	748.3 ± 58.7
Volunteers Mean ± SD	771.4 ± 52.3	787.1 ± 50.7	797.7 ± 60.3	750.0 ± 66.4	658.7 ± 60.3	665.5 ± 42.8	768.1 ± 65.3	713.4 ± 54.1
Pat. vs. Car.	p>0.05	p>0.05	P>0.05	P=0.017 *	P>0.05	P=0.041 *	P>0.05	P>0.05
Pat. vs. Vol.	P=0.006 *	P=0.011 *	P>0.05	P>0.05	P<0.0001*	P<0.0001*	P>0.05	P=0.0002*
Car. vs. Vol.	P>0.05	P>0.05	P>0.05	P>0.05	P>0.05	P>0.05	P>0.05	P>0.05

*) significant difference according to t-test.

Whereas most areas of the cerebral white matter included into this study showed no significant deviations between patients, carriers and normal volunteers, we saw a significant reduction of FA in the anterior parts of the internal capsule on both sides ($p<0.0001$, patients vs. volunteers) which was accompanied by an increased MD reaching significance on the left side only ($p=0.0002$, table 5). A contrary finding (elevation of FA) was observed in the pedunculi cerebri ($p \leq 0.011$), but without significant change of MD.

There were no significant differences of the DTI parameters between carriers and normal volunteers, neither in the white matter nor in the basal ganglia.

Table 6. Spectroscopic results presented as relations of NAA/Cre and Cho/Cre, of patients and carriers. Significance of difference was examined by t-test

	NAA/Cre	Cho/Cre
Patients	1.49 ± 0.18	0.48 ± 0.58
Carriers	1.53 ± 0.22	0.59 ± 0.07
Patients vs. Carriers	P>0.05	P>0.05

Spectroscopy

1H signal voxel spectroscopy of the occipital white matter gave similar results for patients and carriers. For technical reasons, the spectroscopic data from volunteers could not be evaluated.

Volumetry of Cerebral Grey Matter

A two-sample t-test showed reduced grey matter density in the anterior cingulum, mid cingulate cortex and somatosensory areas of the patients compared to sex and age matched controls. No significant increase in gray matter density was found in the patients group.

Functional Imaging of the Resting State

Independent Component Analysis of the whole group of 5 patients and 9 volunteers showed 2 out of 20 components which could correspond to activations of the so-call "default mode network" and /or to "activations" of the motor network. After correlating both components to the values of the dystonia scale as described above and after FEW correction, there was only one "surviving" cluster situated in the middle section of the anterior part of the cingular gyrus (Coordinates of Maximum [CM]: -2/16/26). Group comparison of that component (patients versus volunteers) showed "activations" in a similar, but contralateral area (CM: 10/18/30). The analysis of age-matched pairs (5 patients versus 5 volunteers) showed a similar area of "activation" in the middle section of the anterior part of the cingular gyrus (CM: -6/16/24,

Figure 4) whereas no clusters were present after the FWE correction in the group comparison analysis.

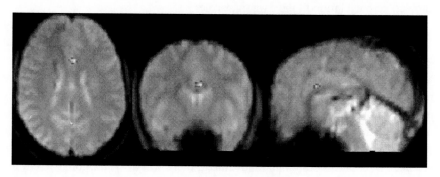

Figure 4. Functional MRI study during resting state shows area within the middle part of the anterior cingular gyrus correlating significantly to dystonia score (p≤0.001). Only some voxels of this cluster remain positive after FWE correction.

However, using non-corrected data thresholded at p≤0.001, we saw "activations" in the left midfrontal region (CM: 4/2/58) corresponding to the posterior part of the Supplementary Motor Area (SMA). The globus pallidus however showed no areas of "activation" which correlated with the degree of dystonia or showed up in the group comparison analysis, even in case of uncorrected data after decreasing the threshold to p≤0.05.

Functional Imaging of Motor Activation

The individual analysis showed activation of the motor system mainly 1 and 2 seconds before the actual hand movement which appeared to be more pronounced in the patient group.

This was confirmed by the correlation analysis: Two seconds before the hand movement actually started, three areas showed a significant (p≤0.001) correlation of activation to the degree of dystonia of the contralateral arm as measured by the Burke Fahn Marsden Scale: the ipsilateral premotor cortex (CM: 30/22/52), a big common cluster in the ipsilateral posterior cingulum and precuneus (CM: 10/-50/32) and the contralateral cerebellum (-14/-42/-50). One second later, the cingulum/precuneus cluster was considerable smaller, but new areas correlating to the clinical score had appeared: the contralateral Supplementary Motor Area (SMA, CM: -6/4/70), premotor cortex (-36/4/36), the motor cortex (-32/-20/60) and the contralateral putamen (CM: -24/-4/8).

One second later, at the actual time of hand movement, the cluster in the SMA and putamen had increased, the M1-cluster had decreased and the other areas showed no correlation to the dystonia scale.

Group comparison (patients vs. volunteers) showed a larger amount of activated voxels at the time of hand contraction in the contralateral precentral gyrus (CM:-30/-22/62) of patients as well as in the paramedian SMA (CM: -4/4/60) and in both putamina (CM: 28/-2/14 and -26/4/8). However, the maximal difference of activation between groups was seen in the primary motor area and the SMA 1 sec before the hand movement started. This maximum appeared earlier (-2 sec) in the premotor cortex, mainly on the contralateral side (CM: -46/20/30) and faded away during the next two seconds. 2 seconds before hand movement, there was also additional activation in the contralateral cerebellum (CM: -16/-40/-50).

However, none of the results of the motor activation study survived the FWE correction procedure.

Again, the globus pallidus showed no areas of "activation" in the correlation or group comparison analysis, even after decreasing the threshold to p≤0.05.

Discussion

Although a number of publication have described the "eye-of-the-tiger" sign as mentioned above, there are some results, which may not be well-known or at least underline existing opinions from radiological case reports and other publications [36, 37].

One is the observation of the presentation of the "tiger's eye" in its early stages. The two youngest patients of 4 and 6 years showed the bright spot in the antero-medial part of the globus pallidus and just a tiny and circumscribed obscuration below it in T2*-imaging which is the most sensible of the applied sequences to show local inhomogeneities of susceptibility.

The hyperintensity is thought to be due to the primary metabolic defect which specifically affects the antero-medial part of the pallidum because of some special metabolic demand or other unknown reason.

This area is not identical with that of first signal reduction, which is situated slightly inferior to the level of the foramen of Monro. There, signal reduction continues with age and reaches a maximum in all sequences. This signal loss is most probably due to accumulation of iron in an area, where the concentration of cystein may be increased, because it cannot be processed further due to the metabolic defect. There are reports that cystein supports oxidation, but also is a strong chelating agent and mobilizes extravascular iron from ferritin [1, 38, 39]. Recently, a defective expression of ferritin and a reduced amount of membrane-associated mRNA-bound iron regulating protein 1 have been described in skin fibroblasts from 3 PKAN patients giving rise to a higher bioactive labile iron pool [40]. Both factors may induce oxidative stress to surrounding cellular membranes.

The hypothesis of at least two components of iron being present in the brain has been raised already by Hallervorden and Spatz (1922 [2]) and is supported by recent MRI findings in the globus pallidus of PKAN patients which were examined in magnetic fields of different strength [41]. Applying a two-compartment model, the authors estimated the content of anti-ferromagnetic iron bound to ferritin as 391 μg/ml (compared to 178 μg/ml in their control group) and of free ferromagnetic iron to 1.1 μg/ml. Supposing that the latter compartment is stored in form of microcristals, the authors question the success of applying chelating agents in the treatment of PKAN, "because chelates cannot eliminate microcristals".

Similar to our results of a non-existing correlation between the extension and the degree of abnormal signal loss in the globus pallidus and the severity of dystonic symptoms, no correlation between the increase in relaxation time after such therapy and the improvement of dystonia has been seen in a pilot study [42].

Our finding of a larger size of the hyperintensity as compared to the dark area in our youngest patients supports the idea that the bright lesion is the first to appear as it is described in a recent publication in a boy of an age of 2 years and 10 months [39]. The obvious concentration of the primary lesion to the globus pallidus by a general metabolic defect is difficult to explain, but shows some parallels to lesions in mitochondrial dysfunctions as Leigh's disease, because the variation of the pantothenate kinase isoenzymes affected in PKAN is the only one with a mitochondrial localization and activity [43].

But how is it possible, that the lesion producing the bright spot, and the signal reduction due to accumulation of iron, start in two different areas? The fact that concentration of iron as judged by the amount of signal reduction is less pronounced in the hyperintense area may be due to the reduced capacity of gliotic scar tissue to mobilize iron from ferritin. But this does not explain the preference of iron to appear first, and later to concentrate always in a region just below the "Eye". One explanation could be that this region is a second though less affected "hot spot" where neurons or special glia cells survive and for some unknown reason initiate the accumulation of iron.

With progressing age, the signal reduction increases in the globus pallidus in PKAN patients as we could demonstrate by the positive correlation between extension of the hypointensity in T2 weighted images and the age of the patients. The globus pallidus is known as an area prone to accumulation of iron also during normal aging [44, 45]. In this context, the absence of the hyperintensity in the anterior part of the globus pallidus seen in six of our patients could well be a secondary phenomenon. There is in fact one report of a signal loss in the "Eye's" area over time [15], and one of our patients experienced a similar signal reduction (although no complete loss) over a period of 5 years [16]. However, scanning at higher magnetic fields which increases the susceptibility effects of ferromagnetic substances may be a second reason for the presence of 6 patients with genetically proven PKAN, but without the full appearance of the "Eye-of-the-Tiger" sign in our series.

Our findings of the varying appearance of the globus pallidus in T1 weighted MRI have not yet been reported in detail. Most of our patients showed a moderate and more diffuse signal elevation in the area corresponding to the hypointensity in T2- and T2 star weighted images. In addition, we saw an important and circumscribed signal reduction inferior to the "Eye" corresponding to the most severe signal loss in T2- and T2 star weightening. These changes can be well explained by the iron accumulation which similar to intravascular contrast medium, shortens T1 relaxation time of cerebral tissue and thus increases signal up to a certain limit [46]. But in case of very high concentrations or cluster-formation, the T1-signal can be destroyed as well.

The area of the "Tiger's Eye" itself mostly presented as a moderate signal reduction in T1 weightening, as one would expect it to occur in gliotic regions with some loss of fat-containing cell membranes. In those cases however, which did not present a clear hyperintensity in T2-weightening, the region of the "Missing Eye" was either diffusely bright as the rest of the globus pallidus, or showed some tiny and moderately hypointense spots which may represent gliotic parts. It may as well be that both the obscuration in T2- and T2 star weightening and the T1-findings, correspond to an unusual severe iron accumulation in this area with a secondary obscuration of the "Eye", or an initially less-pronounced formation of gliosis with a better preserved metabolic capacity to produce cystein and accumulate iron, as described above. More difficult to explain is the bright appearance of the "eye" in T1 weighted images in three of our patients, two from the oldest group, but as well in an 11-year-old boy. Two of them had been scanned in a 1.5 and one in a 3 Tesla field. One possible reason of course could be the T1 time-shortening effect of iron in a rather homogenous distribution and in a concentration not high enough to induce a signal loss.

Although not in the center of the present report, we looked at the involvement of other nuclei apart from the globus pallidus. We did not see any obscuration of the dentate nucleus and an involvement of the red nucleus in two cases only. This is in accordance with previous observations [19]. However, the problems we met to differentiate between normal and abnormal obscurations of the substantia nigra and the subthalamic nucleus have not been reported by others. Even on simultaneous 3D-projections of special susceptibility-weighted series, this differentiation appeared to be difficult. In fact, the differences in the T2 time we found between patients and volunteers were not in the range of 100% as in the case of the globus pallidus, but between 10 and 15%. So we finally decided that only in one case, we could be confident that both nuclei were abnormally hypointense.

This of course does not mean that there are no abnormal iron depositions in the substantia nigra as have been already described by Hallervorden and Spatz in their original report [2]. It only means that at present MR results reporting this still have to be looked upon with special caution. Obviously, the substantia nigra is not affected in the "radiological sense" in very early age, because in our youngest patients both nuclei did not show an abnormal obscuration. But it may get affected (as the subthalamic nucleus is) with further progression, and the course may not be so very different from the globus pallidus. Our data do not allow speculate about a correlation to the clinical expression, although Parkinsonian symptoms have been described in late-onset PKAN cases [47, 48]. It appears worth-while in future to look into this relationship, for example using very high magnetic field imaging and quantitative methods as measurement of T2 time [49, 50].

Another remarkable finding of our study is the presence of a completely developed "Eye-of-the-Tiger" sign in 3 cases from the Dominican Republic, which were found by screening (genetic analysis and imaging) in a group of family members before manifestation of clinical symptoms. This is in contrast to the two youngest symptomatic cases from the USA, where the hyperintensity dominated and the hypointense regions were still small. Obviously, the onset of clinical symptoms does not depend primarily on the accumulation of iron. This result again fits well to the fact that we did not find a significant correlation between the extension of the hypointense area in the globus pallidus representing the area of iron accumulation, and the degree of dystonia. As in the non-affected population, where accumulation of iron in the globus pallidus increases with age [45], PKAN patients show a similar trend, which may be due to their ongoing metabolic dysregulation. However, our findings do not support the idea of the iron accumulation to be the factor which primarily governs the clinical expression of the disease.

The same conclusion applies more or less to the "Tiger's Eye". If this finding represents the lesion responsible for the clinical manifestation, how can we explain those three "preclinical" cases with a fully developed sign in imaging, but with no obvious neurological symptoms? Unfortunately, we obviously have missed the very early stages of the MR manifestation of their lesions. Even our youngest case being four years old, probably presents a chronic defect because an accompanying reduction of diffusion was not seen in the ADC map, as one would expect in the acute stage with intracellular edema. If the acute lesion in the globus pallidus arises some time before the clinical manifestation, which mechanism governs the clinical course?

Looking to other areas of the brain which might be involved in the production of dystonic symptoms in PKAN, we examined the white matter using DTI and spectroscopy, and the grey matter using VBM. Our most remarkable finding was the significantly elevated FA and MD values of the globus pallidus and to a minor degree the slightly elevated FA values of the cerebral peduncle, here without significant changes of MD. This result is remarkable in so far as usually in degenerative white matter disease, both parameters move in opposite directions. A similar observation was reported by Awasthi et al. [20] in the globus pallidus of (although not genetically proven) children with PKAN and by Pfefferbaum et al. [51] in the basal ganglia of the aging brain, but the correlation between relaxivity and MD values was negative in their cases.

We agree with the explanation of both groups that the change in DTI parameters is probably caused by the iron deposits disturbing the local magnetic field. Similar to an increase of gradient strength, diffusing protons covering larger distances will be exposed to greater field changes in the presence of inhomogeneous iron deposits. Thus, they will lose more signal than those protons with restricted diffusion moving perpendicular to some membranes. In this way, a higher index of FA will be calculated which is not based on tissue membrane properties. In a similar way, MD will be increased artificially by the additional impact of local field changes on the signal loss caused by the diffusion gradients. Because of this, changes in DTI parameters and fiber tracking results should be interpreted with extreme caution in areas with disturbances of the local fields, especially in the case of a parallel elevation of both parameters.

In the anterior part of the internal capsule however, we saw a reduction in FA accompanied by an increase in MD, and a minor degree of FA reduction in the thalamus without alterations of MD. In degenerative brain disease, these changes are interpreted as "microstructural alterations of white matter tract integrity" [52]. Because the signal drop caused by the iron deposits is confined to the globus pallidus and the most medial parts of the internal capsule where we did not measure, and because the changes in FA and MD taken from the anterior part of the internal capsule move in opposite directions, we regard this finding as real. The same might apply to the FA reduction of the thalamus. A similar reduction of thalamic FA has been described in patients with different forms of cervical dystonia not suffering from PKAN [53], and in the corresponding white matter tracts to the prefrontal cortex [54] in two variants of primary dystonia. Both structures belong to the output circuits of the internal globus pallidus, but may have been affected in a reactive and secondary manner [24, 55].

We did not see any significant differences between carriers and controls with respect to relaxivity or DTI parameters or spectroscopic values and thus cannot confirm the finding of Sener et al. [21] who reported a significant increase in FA values of the globus pallidus of clinically unaffected (but not genetically screened) siblings from patients with PKAN disease.

In contrast to other degenerative conditions with involvement of the basal ganglia or the thalamus as in Huntington's Disease [56] or Progressive Supranuclear Palsy [57], the white matter otherwise appeared to be normal with respect to DTI parameters and also to the spectroscopic findings. Whereas spectra from the basal ganglia - where we did not measure in order to avoid iron-induced artefacts - showed reduction of the NAA concentration resp. of the NAA/Cre ratio in PKAN patients, spectroscopy of white matter areas have been reported to be normal [17] or were affected only in that one of two siblings who showed a more rapid progression of an otherwise unclassified type of NBIA [58].

VBM of the grey matter showed a reduction of grey matter density in anterior and mid cingular cortex and somatosensory areas in patients with PKAN. Similar studies in other forms of dystonia have given different results depending on the type of disease, but the grey matter density of the globus pallidus was found to be increased in cervical dystonia [59, 60] as well as in focal hand and generalized dystonia, here together with volume increase of frontal parts of the striatum and the medial prefrontal cortex [22]. This phenomenon has been interpreted as an effect of neuroplasticity, which means an increase of cerebral volume due to synaptic formation etc. as a response to increased activity [61]. Our patients however did not show any grey matter volume change of their basal ganglia. As far as the cortex is concerned, results reported in the literature are different. Increases in volume of the primary motor cortex [62] are counterbalanced by volume reduction in the SMA [59] and the primary and sensori-motor cortex, which is hypothesised to lead to a reduced connectivity of these areas to the basal ganglia being responsible for the volume loss [63].

Taken these morphological findings together, there were no great deviations from the normal state, which means that the rest of the brain apart from the globus pallidus seems to be preserved rather well. The pallidal lesion however may remain clinically silent for some time, as shown by our three "preclinical" cases. To look further into the pathophysiologic processes which eventually may result in dystonic symptoms, we have applied the two functional MRI studies described above.

Recording Blood Oxygen Level Dependent (BOLD) contrast images during resting state, we saw an increased activity the middle part of the anterior cingular gyrus in our patients as compared to volunteers. Although subjects were instructed not to move during the functional MRI scanning procedure we cannot exclude involuntary movements in this disease or efforts to suppress dystonic activity. Both might have induced activation in a region belonging to the cingulate motor area. The localization corresponds well to the area of decreased grey matter density seen in our VBM analysis. A second area of increased activity showed up in the posterior SMA but with less statistical significance. Again, there was a correlating VBM finding, although in a more anterior localization. However as always in studies of functional MRI we cannot decide if this area is the primary source of hyperactivity or a reaction to some input from a primary "focus" elsewhere. A similar finding of abnormally increased resting state metabolism in the SMA has been reported in Positron Emission Tomography (PET) studies of patients suffering from primary generalized dystonia and clinically non-manifesting DYT1 carriers [23, 29], together with increased activity in the posterior putamen and globus pallidus and cerebellum. In our cohort however, the globus pallidus was specifically spared from such abnormal activity as compared to the control group.

As with the functional MRI study of the resting state, we here describe the first study about motor activation in dystonia due to PKAN. In general, the activation patterns of our patients resembled those seen in healthy volunteers, and after FWE correction, there were no significant differences left. Nevertheless, we found some important changes of motor activation, which are in accordance with the deviations described in other forms of dystonia as has been outlined in the introduction, but have never been reported in PKAN.

Our motor activation study as well showed some areas of increased activity in patients as compared to the control group, beginning 2 seconds before the actual hand movement, mainly in the contralateral SMA, premotor cortex and cerebellum, then involving the primary motor cortex and finally, at the time of the actual hand movement, spreading to both putamina. This "overactivation" of the motor network is consistent with the view of the dystonic syndrome as an "over-contraction of the primary muscles normally used for a movement, along with overflow contraction of nearby muscles that sometimes antagonize the primary muscles" [24].

Cortical "hyperactivations" have been observed in the majority of fMRI motor activation studies of dystonic patients [24]. They have been shown to be "genotype-related and graded in degree with respect to clinical penetrance" [29]. But also reduced activities of the motor circuits have been reported [64, 65]. In PKAN, the primary lesion undoubtedly is localized in the globus pallidus as demonstrated by the post-mortem and imaging studies described above and our own findings of the primary lesion first to appear as an area of hyperintensity anterior in the medial part of the globus pallidus.

The concept that basal ganglia dysfunction is responsible for the development of dystonia by reduction of feed-back inhibition has been challenged in a way that the cerebellum and brainstem nuclei may be involved as well [66, 67]. In fact, our patients presented some cerebellar "hyperactivation" similar to findings in PET [29, 68] and fMRI studies [69, 70] in patients with writer's cramp. Although we can never be sure about the primary focus which initiates the dystonic movements, reduced pallidal output leading to "disinhibition" of thalamic and cortical motor areas has been identified as a common feature in dystonic conditions by electro-physiologic animal studies as well as during an electrode implantation procedure for Deep Cerebral Stimulation (DBS [71]).

However, two questions remain to be answered: one concerns the latency between the appearance of the lesion and the onset of clinical symptoms as seen in our three "preclinical" cases. Obviously, some other changes have to take place before the "movement overflow" starts. This may be some sort of compensation of the pallidal lesion leading to impaired "surround inhibition" or "impaired modulation of intracortical inhibition" of the somato-sensory and motor system, which has been suggested as a maladaptive learning process in patients suffering mainly from focal hand dystonia [25, 72-74]. An impairment of the homeostatic mechanisms that stabilize excitability levels within a useful dynamic range" [28] in the sense of "maladaptive plasticity" [75] has been proposed as underlying cause.

The other open question is that about the effectiveness of DBS of the globus pallidus in dystonia, which might further reduce the already impaired output of this nucleus. Nevertheless, in DTY1 dystonia, DBS seems to work rather well, possibly because of a normalization effect on the electro-physiologic discharge pattern as shown in a mice model [55]. In PKAN however, initial optimistic reports [76, 77] have been questioned by the results of a multicenter study which failed to show a positive long-lasting effect after some initial improvement [78], and the ventral nuclei of the thalamus have been suggested as an alternative target [65].

Conclusion

We could confirm the presence of a "hyperactivation" of the motor network in patients suffering from PKAN as it has been described in other forms of dystonia. The fact that the lesion of this metabolic condition originates in the globus pallidus, supports the concept that at least in PKAN, the reduced (inhibitory) activity of this nucleus is responsible as a primary factor, although this may not apply to other forms of dystonia. However, a lesion or a further electrophysiologic inhibition of the pallidal activity wouldn't make sense. So it is not surprising that former interventions placing lesions directly into the globus pallidus [79] did not improve the dystonic symptoms over time. As a consequence, the application of DBS to the pallidal output areas should be re-considered, as mentioned above.

Two other important results of the study with therapeutic implications remain to be mentioned: one is the lack of correlation of the obscuration seen with the "Eye-of-the-Tiger" sign to the progression of symptoms, which questions the role of imaging of the hypointensity as a parameter of disease progression and as well the effect of an anti-chelating therapy as it is conducted now with support of the European Union (TIRCON trial). The other one is the latency between the first appearance of the lesion seen in MRI, and the clinical manifestation of dystonic movements. If during this time really a maladaptive compensation process is going on, there might be a possibility to counterbalance this development. As in our cases, genetically positive children might be detected by screening test of affected families, and early training programs might be able to prolong the period of latency or hopefully the course of the disease, because outside the globus pallidus, there is no evidence of severe structural damage in these patients.

Acknowledgments

The authors like to thank S. Hayflick, MD, University of Oregon/USA, for contributing scan data from 9 of her patients, and CEDIMAT, Santo Domingo, Dominican Republic, for logistic and financial support of the study.

References

[1] Hayflick, SJ. Unraveling the Hallervorden-Spatz syndrome: pantothenate kinase-associated neurodegeneration is the name. *Curr. Opin. Pediatr.,* 2003, 15, 572-577.

[2] Hallervorden, J; Spatz H. Eigenartige Erkrankung im extrapyramidalen System mit besonderer Beteiligung des Globus pallidus und der Substantia nigra. *Z Gesamte Neurol. Psychiatr., 1922,* 79, 254-302.

[3] Hayflick, SJ; Westaway, SK; Levinson, B; Zhou, B; Johnson, MA; Ching, KH; Gitschier, J. Genetic, clinical, and radiographic delineation of Hallervorden-Spatz syndrome. *N. Engl. J. Med.,* 2003, 348, 33-40.

[4] Hartig, MB; Hörtnagel, K; Garavaglia, B; Zorzi, G; Kmiec, T; Klopstock, T; Rostasy, K; Svetel, M; Kostic, VS; Schuelke, M; Botz, E; Weindl, A; Novakovic, I; Nardocci, N; Prokisch, H; Meitinger, T. Genotypic and sphenotypic spectrum of PANK2 mutations in patients with neurodegeneration with brain iron accumulation. *Ann. Neurol.,* 2006, 59, 248-256.

[5] Zhou, B; Westaway, SK; Levinson, B; Johnson, MA; Gitschier, J; Hayflick, SJ. A novel pantothenate kinase gene (PANK2) is defective in Hallervorden-Spatz syndrome. *Nat. Genet.,* 2001, 28, 345-349.

[6] Gregory, A; Hayflick, SJ. Neurodegeneration with brain iron accumulation. *Folia Neuropathol.,* 2005, 43, 286-296.

[7] Pellecchia, MT; Valente, EM; Cif, L; Salvi, S; Albanese, A; Scarano, V; Bonuccelli, U; Bentivoglio, AR; D'Amico, A; Marelli, C; Di Giorgio, A; Coubes, P; Barone, P; Dallapiccola; B. The diverse phenotype and genotype of pantothenate kinase-associated neurodegeneration. *Neurology,* 2005, 64, 1810-1812.

[8]   Leoni, V, Strittmatter, L; Zorzi, G; Zibordi, F; Dusi, S; Garavaglia, B; Venco, P; Caccia, C; Souza, AL; Deik, A; Clish, CB; Rimoldi, M; Ciusani, E; Bertini, E; Nardocci, N; Mootha, VK, Tiranti, V. Metabolic consequences of mitochondrial coenzyme A deficiency in patients with PANK2 mutations. *Mol. Genet. Metab.,* 2012, 105, 463-471.

[9]   Kruer, MC; Hiken, M; Gregory, A; Malandrini, A; Clark, D; Hogarth, P; Grafe, M; Hayflick, SJ; Woltjer, RL.Novel histiopathologic findings in molecularly-confirmed pantothenate kinate-associated neurodegeneration. *Brain,* 2011, 134, 947-958.

[10]   Bindu, PS; Desai, S; Shehanaz, KE; Nethravathy, M; Pal, PK. Clinical heterogeneity in Hallervorden-Spatz syndrome: a clinicoradiological study in 13 patients from South India. Brain Dev 2006, 28, 343-347.

[11]   Trussart, V; Leboucq, N; Carlander, B; Billiard, M; Castan, P. Hallervorden-Spatz syndrome and MRI: the "tiger's eye". *J. Neuroradiol.,* 1993, 20, 70-75.

[12]   Gordon, N. Pantothenate kinase-associated neurodegeneration Hallervorden-Spatz syndrome. *Eur. J. Paediatr. Neurol.,* 2002, 6, 243-247

[13]   Hayflick, SJ; Hartman, M; Coryell, J; Gitschier, J; Rowley H. Brain MRI in neurodegeneration with brain iron accumulation with and without PANK2 mutations. *AJNR Am. J. Neuroradiol.,* 2006, 27, 1230-1233.

[14]   Kumar, N; Boes, CJ; Babovic-Vuksanovic, D; Boeve, BF. The "eye-of-the-tiger" sign is not pathognomonic of the PANK2 mutation. *Arch. Neurol.,* 2006, 63, 292-3.

[15]   Baumeister, FA; Auer, DP; Hörtnagel, K; Freisinger, P; Meitinger, T. The eye-of-the-tiger sign is not a reliable disease marker for Hallervorden-Spatz syndrome. *Neuropediatrics,* 2005, 36, 221-222.

[16]   Delgado, RF; Sanchez, PR; Speckter, H; Then, EP; Jimenez, R; Oviedo, J; Dellani, PR; Foerster, B; Stoeter, P. Missense PANK2 mutation without "Eye of the tiger" sign: MR findings in a large group of patients with pantothenate kinase-associated neurodegeneration (PKAN). *J. Magn. Reson. Imaging.,* 2012, 35, 788-794

[17]   Hájek, M; Adamovicová, M; Herynek, V; Skoch, A; Jírů, F; Krepelová, A; Dezortová, M. MR relaxometry and 1H MR spectroscopy for the determination of iron and metabolite concentrations in PKAN patients. *Eur. Radiol.,* 2005, 15, 1060-1068.

[18] Szumowski J, Bas, E; Gaarder, K; Schwarz, E; Erdogmus, D; Hayflick, S. Measurement of brain iron distribution in Hallervorden-Spatz syndrome. *J. Magn. Res. Imaging.*, 2010, 31, 482-489.

[19] McNeill, A; Birchall, D; Hayflick, SJ; Gregory, A; Schenk, JF; Zimmerman, EA; Shang, H; Miyajima, H; Chinnery, PF. T2* and FSE MRI distinguishes four subtypes of neurodegeneration with brain iron accumulation. *Neurology,* 2008, 70, 1614-1619.

[20] Awasthi, R; Gupta, RK; Trivedi, R; Singh, JK; Paliwal, VK; Rathore RK. Diffusion tensor MR imaging in children with pantothenate kinase-associated neurodegeneration with brain iron accumulation and their siblings. *AJNR Am. J. Neuroradiol.*, 2010, 31, 442-447.

[21] Sener RN. Pantothen kinate-associated neurodegeneration: MR imaging, proton spectroscopy, and diffusion MR imaging findings. *AJNR Am. J. Neuroradiol.*, 2003, 24, 1690-1693.

[22] Egger, K; Mueller, J; Schocke, M; Brenneis, C; Rinnerthaler, M; Seppi, K; Trieb, T; Wenning, GK; Hallett, M; Poewe, W. Voxel based morphometry reveals specific grey matter changes in primary dystonia. *Mov. Disord.*, 2007, 22, 1538-1542.

[23] Asanuma, K; Carbon-Correll, M; Eidelberg, D. Neuroimaging in human dystonia. *J. Med. Invest.*, 2005, 52 Suppl, 272-279.

[24] Neychev, VK; Gross, RE; Lehéricy, S; Lehéricy, S; Hess, EJ; Jinnah, HA. The functional neuroanatomy of dystonia. *Neurobiol. Dis.*, 2011, 42, 185-201.

[25] Tamura, Y; Matsuhashi, M; Lin, P; Ou, B; Vorbach, S; Kakigi, R; Hallett, M. Impaired intracortical inhibition in the primary somatosensory cortex in focal hand dystonia. *Mov. Disord.*, 2008, 23, 558-565.

[26] Lin, PT; Hallett, M. The pathophysiology of focal hand dystonia. *J. Hand Ther.*, 2009, 22, 109-113.

[27] Rosenkranz, K; Butler, K; Williamon, A; Cordivari, C; Lees, AJ; Rothwell, JC. Sensorimotor reorganization by proprioceptive training in musician's dystonia and writer's cramp. *Neurology,* 2008, 70, 304-315.

[28] Quartarone, A; Rizzo, V; Bagnato, S; Morgante, F; Sant'Angelo, A; Romano, M; Crupi, D; Girlanda, P; Rothwell, JC; Siebner, HR. Homeostatic-like plasticity of the primary motor hand area is impaired in focal hand dystonia. *Brain,* 2005, 128 1943-1950.

[29] Carbon, M; Eidelberg, D. Abnormal structure-function relationships in hereditary dystonia. *Neuroscience,* 2009, 164, 220-229.

[30] Stoeter, P; Rodriguez-Raecke, R; Vilchez, C; Perez-Then, E; Speckter, H;
      Oviedo, J; Roa-Sanchez, P. Motor activation in patients with
      pantothenate kinase-associated neurodegeneration: a functional magnetic
      resonance imaging study. *Parkinsonism Relat. Disord.*, 2012, 18, 1007-
      1010.

[31] Fermin-Delgado, R; Roa-Sanchez, P; Speckter, H; Perez-Then, E;
      Rivera-Mejia, D; Foerster, B; Stoeter, P. Involvement of globus pallidus
      and   midbrain   nuclei   in   pantothenate   kinase-associated
      neurodegeneration: measurement of T2 and T2* time. *Clin.
      Neuroradiol.*, 2013, 23, 11-15.

[32] Vilchez-Abreu, C; Roa-Sanchez, P; Fermin-Delgado, R ; Speckter, H;
      Perez-Then, E; Oviedo, J; Stoeter, P. El signo del "Ojo del Tigre" en
      resonancia magnética: cambios relacionados con la edad. *An. Radiol.
      Mex.*, 2013, in press.

[33] Senegas, J; Bos, C; Dahnke, H. Determining precision of relaxation time
      measurements: application to T2 mapping. ISMRM 2008; 16th
      Scientific Meeting, Toronto/Can. Proceedings p. 1421.

[34] Dellani, PR ; Glaser, M ; Wille, PR ; Vucurevic, G; Stadie, A;
      Bauermann, T; Tropine, A; Perneczky, A; von Wangenheim, A; Stoeter,
      P. White matter fiber tracking computation based on diffusion tensor
      imaging for clinical applications. *J. Digit. Imaging*, 2007, 20, 88-97.

[35] Müller, MJ; Mazanek, M; Weibrich, C; Dellani, PR; Stoeter, P;
      Fellgiebel, A. Distribution characteristics, reproducibility, and precision
      of region of interest-based hippocampal diffusion tensor imaging
      measures. *AJNR Am. J. Neuroradiol.*, 2006, 27, 440-446.

[36] Sethi, KD; Adams, RJ; Loring, DW; El Gammal, T;. Hallervorden-Spatz
      syndrome: clinical and magnetic resonance imaging correlations. *Ann.
      Neurol.*, 1988, 24, 692-694.

[37] Guillerman, RP. The Eye-of-the-Tiger sign. *Radiology*, 2000, 217, 895-
      896.

[38] Schipper, HM Neurodegeneration with brain iron accumulation -
      Clinical syndromes and neuroimaging. *Biochim. Biophys. Acta.*, 2012,
      1822, 350-360.

[39] Rossi, D; De Grandis, E; Barzaghi, C; Mascaretti, M; Garavaglia, B;
      Zanotto, E; Morana, G; Biancheri, R. Early-onset neurodegeneration
      with brain iron accumulation due to PANK2 mutation. *Brain Dev.*, 2011,
      34, 536-538.

[40] Campanalla, A, Privitera D; Guaraldo, M; Rovelli, E; Barzaghi, C;
      Garavaglia, B; Santambrogio, P; Cozzi, A; Levi,S. Skin fibrobalsts from

pantothenate kinase-associated neurodegeneration patients show altered cellular oxidative status and have defective iron-handling properties. *Hum. Mol. Genet.*, 2012, 21, 4049-4059.

[41] Dezortova, M; Herynek, V; Krssak, M; Kronerwetter, C; Trattnig, S; Hajek,M. Two forms of iron as an intrinsic contrast agent in the basal ganglia of PKAN patients. *Contrast Media Mol. Imaging*, 2012, 7, 509-515.

[42] Zorzi, G; Zibordi, F; Chiapparini, L; Bertini, E; Russo, L; Piga, A; Longo, F; Garavaglia, B; Aquino, D; Savoiardo, M; Solari, A; Nardocci, N. Iron-related MRI images in patients with pantothenate kinase-associated neurodegeneration (PKAN) treated with deferiprone: results of a phase II pilot trial. *Mov. Disord.*, 2011, 26, 1756-1759.

[43] Hörtnagel,K; Prokisch,H; Meitinger, T. An isoform of hPANK2, deficient in pantothenate-kinase associated neurodegeneration, localizes to mmitochondria. *Hum. Mol. Genet.*, 2003, 12, 321-327.

[44] Vymazal, J; Brooks, RA; Patronas, N; Hajek, M; Bulte, JW; Di Chiro, G. Magnetic resonance imaging of brain iron in health and disease. *J. Neurol. Sci.*, 1995, 134 Suppl, 19-26.

[45] Aquino, D; Bizzi, A; Grisoli, M; Garavaglia, B, Bruzzone, MG; Nardocci, M; Savoiardo, M; Chiapparini, L. Age-related iron deposition in the basal ganglia: quantitative analysis in healthy subjects. *Radiology*, 2009, 252, 165-172.

[46] Vymazal, J; Brooks, RA; Baumgarner, C; Tran, V; Katz, D; Bulte, JW; Bauminger, R; Di Chiro, G. The relation between brain iron and NMR relaxation times: an in vitro study. *Magn. Reson Med.*, 1996, 35, 56-61.

[47] Antonini, A; Goldwurm, S; Benti, R; Prokisch, H; Ebhardt, M; Cilia, R; Zini, M; Righini, A; Cossu, G; Pezzoli, G. Genetic, clinical, and imaging characterization of one patient with late-onset, slowly progressive, pantothenate kinase-associated neurodegeneration. *Mov. Disord.*, 2006, 21, 417-418.

[48] Seo, JH; Song, SK, Lee PH. A novel PANK2 mutation in a patient with atypical pantothenate kinase-associated neurodegeneration presenting with adult-onset Parkinsonism. *J. Clin. Neurol.*, 2009, 5, 192-194.

[49] Cho, ZH; Min, HK; Oh, SH; Han, JY; Park, CW; Chi, JG; Kim, YB; Paek, SH; Lozano, AM; Lee, KH. Direct visualization of deep brain stimulation targets in Parkinson disease with the use of 7-tesla magnetic resonance imaging. *J. Neurosurg.*, 2010, 113, 639-647.

[50] Deistung, A; Schäfer, A; Schweser, F; Biedermann, U; Turner, R; Reichenbach, JR. Toward in-vivo histology: a comparison of quantitative susceptibility mapping (QSM) with magnitude-, phase-, and R2*imaging at ultra-high magnetic field strength. *NeuroImage,* 2013, 65, 299-314.

[51] Pfefferbaum, A; Adalsteinsson, E; Rohlfing, T; Sullivan, EV. MRI estimates of brain iron concentration in normal aging: comparison of field-dependent (FDRI) and phase (SWI) methods. *Neuroimage,* 2009, 47, 493-500.

[52] Fellgiebel, A; Wille, P; Müller, MJ; Winterer, G; Scheurich, A; Vucurevic, G; Schmidt, LG; Stoeter, P. Ultrastructural hippocampal and white matter alterations in mild cognitive impairment: a diffusion tensor imaging study. *Dement. Geriatr. Cogn. Disord.,* 2004, 18, 101-108.

[53] Bonilha,L; de Vries, PM; Hurd, MW; Rorden, C; Morgan, PS; Besenski, N; Bergmann, KJ; Hinson, VK. Disrupted thalamic prefrontal pathways in patients with idiopathic dystonia. *Parkinsonism. Relat. Disord.,* 2009, 15, 64-67.

[54] Argyelan, M; Carbon, M; Niethammer, M; Ulug, AM; Voss, HU; Bressman, SB; Dhawan, V; Eidelberg, D. Cerebellothalamocortical connectivity regulates penetrance in dystonia. *J. Neurosci.,* 2009, 29, 9740-9747.

[55] DeLong, M; Wichmann, T. Circuits and circuit disorders of the basal ganglia. *Arch. Neurol.,* 2007, 64, 20-24.

[56] Rosas, HD; Tuch, DS; Hevelone, ND; Zaleta, AK; Vangel, M; Hersch, SM; Salat, DH. Diffusion tensor imaging in presymptomatic and early Huntington's disease: Selective white matter pathology and its relationship to clinical measures. *Mov. Disord.,* 2006, 21, 1317-1325.

[57] Erbetta, A; Mandelli, ML; Savoiardo, M; Savoiardo, M; Grisoli, M; Bizzi, A; Soliveri, P; Chiapparini, L; Prioni, S; Bruzzone, MG; Girotti, F.. Diffusion tensor imaging shows different topographic involvement of the thalamus in progressive supranuclear palsy and corticobasal degeneration. *AJNR Am. J. Neuroradiol.,* 2009, 30, 1482-1487.

[58] Kitis, O; Tekgul, H; Erdemir, G; Polat, M; Serdaroglu, G; Tosun, A; Coker, M; Gokben, S. Identification of axonal involvement in Hallervorden-Spatz disease with magnetic resonance spectroscopy. *J. Neuroradiol.,* 2006, 33, 129-132.

[59] Draganski, B; Thun-Hohenstein, C; Bogdahn, U; Winkler, J; May, A. Motor circuit grey matter changes in idiopathic cervical dystonia. *Neurology,* 2003, 61, 1228-1231.

[60] Draganski, B; Schneider, SA; Fiorio, M; Klöppel, S; Gambarin, M; Tinazzi, M; Ashburner, J; Bhatia, KP; Frackowiak, RS. Genotype-phenotype interactions in primary dystonias revealed by differential changes in brain structure. *NeuroImage,* 2009, 47, 1141-1147.

[61] Draganski, B; May, A. Training-induced structural changes in the adult human brain. *Behav. Brain Res.,* 2008, 192, 137-142.

[62] Granert, O; Peller, M; Jabusch, HC; Altenmüller, E; Siebner, HR. Sensorimotor skills and focal dystonia are linked to putaminal grey-matter volume in pianists. *J. Neurol. Neurosurg. Psychiatry,* 2011, 82, 1225-1231.

[63] Pantano, P; Totaro, P; Fabbrini, G; Raz, E; Contessa, GM; Tona, F; Colosimo, C; Berardelli, A. A transverse and longitudinal MR imaging voxel-based morphometry study in patients with primary cervical dystonia. *AJNR Am. J. Neuroradiol.,* 2011, 32, 81-84.

[64] Haslinger, B; Erhard, P; Dresel, C; "Silent event-related" fMRI reveals reduced sensorimotor activation in laryngeal dystonia. *Neurology,* 2005, 65, 1562-1569.

[65] Dresel, C; Haslinger, B; Castrop, F. Silent event-related fMRI reveals deficient motor and enhanced somatosensory activation in orofacial dystonia. *Brain,* 2006 129, 36-46.

[66] Bostan, AC; Strick, PL. The cerebellum and basal ganglia are interconnected. *Neuropsychol. Rev.,* 2010, 20, 261-270.

[67] Hendrix, CM; Vitek, JL. Toward a network model of dystonia. *Ann N Y Acad. Sci.,* 2012, 1265, 46-55.

[68] Odergren, T; Stone-Elander, S; Ingvar, M. Cerebral and cerebellar activation in correlation to the action-induced dystonia in writer's cramp. *Mov. Disord.,* 1998, 13, 497-508.

[69] Preibisch, C; Berg, D; Hofmann, E; Cerebral activation patterns in patients with writer's cramp: a functional magnetic resonance imaging study. *J. Neurol.,* 2001, 248, 10-17.

[70] Hu, XY; Wang, L; Liu, H; Zhang, SZ. Functional magnetic resonance imaging study of writer's cramp. *Chin. Med. J. (Engl),* 2006, 119, 1263-1271.

[71] Nambu, A; Chiken, S; Shashidharan, P; Nishibayashi, H; Ogura, M; Kakishita, K; Tanak, S; Tachibana, Y; Kita, H; Itakura, T. Reduced pallidal output causes dystonia. Frontiers Syst Neurosci 2011, 5, article 89, 1-6 (www.frontiersin.org).

[72] Tinazzi, M; Priori, A; Bertolasi, L; Frasson, E; Mauguière, F; Fiaschi, A. Abnormal central integration of a dual somatosensory input in dystonia. Evidence for sensory overflow. *Brain,* 2000, 123, 42-50.

[73] Sohn, YH; Hallett, M. Disturbed surround inhibition in focal hand dystonia. *Ann. Neurol.,* 2004, 56, 595-599.

[74] Stinear, CM; Byblow, WD. Impaired modulation of intracortical inhibition in focal hand dystonia. *Cereb. Cortex.,* 2004, 14, 555-561.

[75] Altenmüller, E; Jabusch HC. Focal dystonia in musicians: phenomenology, pathophysiology and triggering factors. *Eur. J. Neurol.,* 2010, 17 Suppl 1, 31-36.

[76] Krause, M; Fogel, W; Kloss, M; Rasche, D; Volkmann,J; Tronnier,V. Pallidal stimulation for dystonia. *Neurosurgery,* 2004, 55, 1361-1368.

[77] Umemura, A; Jaggi, JL, Dolinskas, CA; Stern, MB; Baltuch, GH. Pallidal deep brain stimulation for longstanding severe dystonia in Hallervorden-Spatz syndrome. *J. Neurosurg.,* 2004, 100, 706-709.

[78] Timmermann, L; Pauls, KA; Wieland, K; Jech R; Kurlemann, G; Sharma, N; Gill, SS; Haenggeli, CA; Hayflick, SJ; Hoghart, P; Leenders, KL; Limousin, P; Malanga, CJ; Moro, E; Ostrem, JL; Revilla, FJ; Santens, P; Schnitzler, A; Tisch, S; Valldeoriola, F; Vesper, J; Volkmann, J; Woitalla, D; Peker, S. Dystonia in neurodegeneration with brain iron accumulation: outcome of bilateral pallidal stimulation. *Brain,* 2010, 133, 701-712

[79] Balas, I; Kovacs, N; Hollody, K. Staged bilateral stereotactic pallidothalamotomy for life-threatening dystonia in a child with Hallervorden-Spatz disease. *Mov. Disord.,* 2006, 21, 82-85.

In: Globus Pallidus   ISBN: 978-1-62948-367-2
Editors: C.R. Gordon, T.G. Abbadelli   © 2013 Nova Science Publishers, Inc.

Chapter 2

Anatomofunctional Territories and Pathophysiological Relations in Globus Pallidus

*Eun-Jung Lee and Sang Ryong Jeon**

Department of Neurosurgery, Asan Medical Center,
University of Ulsan College of Medicine, Seoul, Korea

Abstract

The very fine somatotopic arrangement of the cortico-basal-ganglia-thalamo-cortical circuit has been extensively detailed in anatomical and physiological studies. Like other basal ganglia, the globus pallidus (GP) maintains three anatomofunctional territories, which are referred to as the sensorimotor territory (for processing sensory and motor information); associative territory (cognitive information); and limbic territory (emotional and motivational information). Thus, movement disorders: dystonia and dyskinesia, cognitive disorders: attention deficit with or without hyperactivity, and stereotyped behaviors can develop because of GP dysfunction. GP dysfunction is crucial to dystonia according to neurophysiological studies, functional imaging data, and animal models.

* Corresponding author: Sang Ryong Jeon, M.D., Ph.D. Address: Department of Neurological Surgery, Asan Medical Center, University of Ulsan College of Medicine, 388-1 Pungnap-2dong, Songpa-gu, Seoul 138-736, Korea. Tel: (+)82-2-3010-3562. E-mail: srjeon@amc.seoul.kr.

Underactivity of the internal segment of GP - but above all irregularities in pallidal activity – has been emphasized as part of the pathophysiology of idiopathic dystonia, including overall increased direct putaminopallidal activity and reduced subthalamointernal pallidal input. GP lesions are also associated with behavioral disorders, such as attention deficit hyperactivity disorder or obsessive-compulsive disorder, if damage occurs in the associative and limbic territories respectively. In this chapter, we review the findings of several important studies on the effects of GP lesions in animals and humans and discuss the role GP plays in the pathophysiology of dystonia, cognitive, and behavioral disorders.

Introduction

The globus pallidus (GP) is one of the output nuclei that comprises the basal ganglia and relays the final signals to targets outside the basal ganglia. It has been reported that GP dysfunction is highly associated with the pathophysiology of movement disorders such as Parkinson's disease (PD) and dystonia [1-14]. Thus, GP is an important therapeutic target when applying stereotactic lesioning and deep brain stimulation (DBS) for the treatment of PD and dystonia. However, it has been reported that cognitive, behavioral, and emotional dysfunction can develop in PD patients who undergo pallidotomy or DBS, as well as marked motor improvement [15-19]. In fact, the basal ganglia participates in many neuronal pathways, and its functions are not restricted to the motor behavior: The basal ganglia is also involved in emotional, motivational, associative and cognitive functions [20-25]. Like other basal ganglia, GP maintains the three anatomofunctional territories, which are known as the sensorimotor, associative, and limbic territories [4, 20, 26-34]. Comprehensive knowledge of the functional anatomy and the roles of GP will be useful for clinicians to understand not only the pathophysiology of movement disorders, but also behavioral disorders such as attention deficit hyperactivity disorder (ADHD) and obsessive-compulsive disorder (OCD) [4, 35]. Additional research will also facilitate the development of precise targets, efficacious surgical interventions with fewer adverse effects, and novel strategies for the treatment of movement and behavioral disorders.

The Regional Anatomy of the Globus Pallidus

The GP lies just medial to the putamen. Globus pallidus (or pallidum) means "pale globe", and it was so named because it contains a greater proportion of myelinated fibers and appears paler than fresh putamen specimens. GP is divided by a vertically oriented sheet of white matter - the medial or internal medullary lamina - into internal (GPi) and external (GPe) segments. The superior and medial aspect of the GP is in contact with the internal capsule, which rostrally separates it from the head of the caudate nucleus and the anterior horn of the lateral ventricle and caudally from the anterolateral surface of the thalamus (Figure 1A).

The superomedial surface of the GP is also separated from the thalamus by the subthalamic nucleus (STN) and the zona incerta in the mid and posterior portions. The caudal end of the STN overlaps with the rostral tip of the substantia nigra. Anteriorly, the inferior surface of the GP is adjacent to the substantial innominate and the more laterally placed fibers of the anterior commissure.

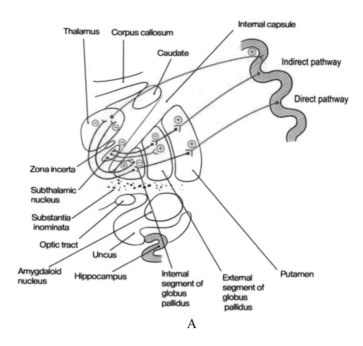

A

Figure 1. Continued on next page.

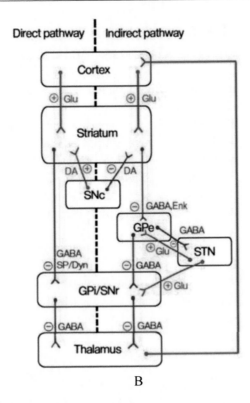

B

Figure 1. Regional anatomy of basal ganglia and internal connections, showing the direct and indirect pathways. (A) Schematic coronal section of the basal ganglia at the level of the hypothalamic nucleus which shows relation with surrounding structures (B) Schematic diagram of the direct and indirect pathways in the basal ganglia-cortex circuit. DA, dopamine; Glu, glutamate; Enk, enkephalin; SP, substance P; SNc, substantia nigra pars compacta; SNr, substantia nigra pars reticulata; GPe, external segment of globus pallidus; GPi, internal segment of globus pallidus; STN, subthalamic nucleus.

The hypothalamus lies medial to this area. More caudally, the inferior surface of the GP is closely related to the optic tract, which winds around the lateral aspect of the cerebral peduncle to the lateral geniculate body. This part of the inferior surface of the GP is also adjacent to the amygdaloid nuclear complex and the medial temporal lobe, which contains the tail of the caudate nucleus, stria terminalis, hippocampus, fornix, and the temporal horn of the lateral ventricle. The caudate nucleus, stria terminalis, and fornix all curve caudally, superiorly, and then rostrally to follow the lateral ventricle and are closely related to the GP on its rostromedial aspect at the tip of the anterior horn of the lateral ventricle [36].

Cortico-Basal ganglia-Thalamo-Cortical Circuits

The basal ganglia essentially consist of an input zone, the striatum (putamen, caudate nucleus, and nucleus accumbens), and an output zone (GPi and the substantia nigra pars reticulata (SNr)) [37, 38].

Most of the cortical inputs to the striatum are excitatory and use glutamate as the neurotransmitter. Another important input to the striatum is from the substantia nigra pars compacta (SNc). The dopaminergic nigrostriatal pathway either excites or inhibits certain cells in the striatum, whereas the output pathways from GPi and SNr are inhibitory and use gamma-aminobutyric acid (GABA) as the neurotransmitter (Figure 1B). The main output pathways are to the ventrolateral (VL) and ventroanterior (VA) nuclei of the thalamus via the thalamic fasciculus. The more anterior parts of the thalamic fasciculus carry outputs from the basal ganglia to the anterior portion of VL nuclei, while the more posterior parts of the thalamic fasciculus carry cerebellar outputs to the posterior VL nuclei. Thalamic neurons carry information from the basal ganglia to the entire frontal lobe. However, information for motor control travels mainly to the premotor cortex, supplementary motor area, and primary motor cortex. Some other basal ganglia outputs are also carried to other thalamic nuclei. These include both intralaminar nuclei (centromedian and parafascicular), which project back to the striatum, and the mediodorsal nucleus (MD), which is primarily involved in the association and limbic pathways.

There are two predominant pathways connecting input to output nuclei that pass through the basal ganglia. The direct pathway travels from the striatum directly to the GPi or SNr. The indirect pathway takes a detour from the striatum, first to the GPe and then to the STN before finally reaching the GPi or SNr. For simplicity, only the pathways through the putamen and GPi are shown in (Figure 1A). Similar pathways also exist in the caudate and the SNr. Striatal projection neurons for both pathways are primarily inhibitory spiny neurons, which contain the neurotransmitter GABA. In the direct pathway, the spiny striatal neurons project to the GPi (and SNr) and contain the peptide substance P and dynorphin in addition to GABA. Output neurons from the GPi and SNr to the thalamus are also inhibitory and contain GABA. In the indirect pathway, striatal neurons project to the GPe and contain the inhibitory neurotransmitter GABA as well as the peptide enkephalin. GPe neurons, in turn, send inhibitory GABAergic projections to the STN.

Excitatory glutamate-containing neurons in the STN project to the GPi and SNr. Finally, both in the direct and indirect pathways, the outputs from these nuclei to the thalamus are inhibitory and mediated by GABAergic neurotransmission. Figure 1B shows that the net effect of the excitatory input from the cortex via the direct pathway is to excite the thalamus, which in turn facilitates movements through its connections with the motor and premotor cortices. On the other hand, the net effect of excitation of the indirect pathway is to inhibit the thalamus, thereby inhibiting movement through connections back to the cortex.

Both pathways demonstrate antagonistic effects on the output of the basal ganglia: the direct pathway sends inhibitory input to the GPi and SNr, whereas the indirect pathway results in excitatory input to them. The dual projections from the output nuclei of the basal ganglia to the different nuclei of the thalamus are organized in parallel and somatotopically [26, 39], while, again, thalamic neurons send convergent inputs to the same cortical areas [40].

The current hypothesis regarding the functions of the basal ganglia suggests that normal motor behavior depends on balancing the information processes of the direct and indirect pathways between the striatum and pallidum; imbalance between the two pathways induces movement disorders. Such an imbalance must evoke abnormal activity in the output nuclei (i.e., the GPi and SNr), which may occur via changes in GABA content and GABA receptors [41, 42].

Functional Territories of the Basal Ganglia

The basal ganglia participate in many neuronal pathways, and their functions are not restricted to motor behavior. Basal ganglia also demonstrate emotional, motivational, associative, and cognitive functions [20, 22, 43]. It is well established that every nucleus in the basal ganglia can be divided into three anatomofunctional territories: sensorimotor territory (for processing sensory and motor information); associative territory (cognitive information); and limbic territory (emotional and motivational information) [20, 27, 31].

One territory of one nucleus in the basal ganglia projects to the corresponding territory of another nucleus, although overlapping projections exists. Thus, each information pathway involved in motor, associative, and limbic function maintains segregated parallel subloops through the striatum, GPi, GPe, STN, and SNr within the cortico-basal ganglia-thalamo-cortical circuit. In addition, these segregated parallel loops appear to demonstrate a strict somatotopic organization [20, 21, 44].

Although these anatomofunctional territories occupy distinct regions, they should be understood as a continuum rather than subdivisions with strict boundaries [27, 31]. Information does converge at the level of the GP, SNr [26], and thalamus [45] and within different nuclei via axonal collateralization [46]. It is likely that parallel but intermingled mechanisms cause the diverse symptomatology that presents in basal ganglia disease [47].

Anatomofunctional Territories and Functional Segregation in the Globus Pallidus

The distribution of striatopallidal projections is maintained within the GP between the three territories [26, 28-30, 32, 33]. According to extensive anatomical and physiological studies on primates, the GPi can be subdivided into motor, associative, and limbic territories, as mentioned above, and each territory is located in the ventrolateral two-thirds, dorsomedial one-third, and medial tip of the GPi, respectively (Figure 2A) [29, 31, 48-50].

Likewise, the GPe has the three parts in these territories: the sensorimotor territory in the posterior and lateral aspect of the GPe; associative territory in the more anterior and medial part of the GPe; limbic territory in the most anterior, medial and ventral part of the GPe [4]. Francois et al. (2004) demonstrated that various abnormal movements and behavioral disorders can be provoked in monkeys by microinjection of bicuculline (Bic), an antagonist of the GABAergic receptor; however, this is dependent on the site of injection into the anatomofunctional part of the GPe [3].

As described above, inputs originating from sensorimotor, associative and limbic cortices remain segregated along their respective channels and innervate to specific areas [20, 31, 39, 51, 52]. The corticostriatal pathway is, therefore, composed of three channels: a sensorimotor channel that projects from the primary motor, premotor, and supplementary motor cortices to the postcommissural putamen [53, 54]; an associative channel that projects from associative cortical areas, including dorsolateral prefrontal and lateral orbitofrontal cortices to the caudate nucleus and precommissural putamen [38, 55-57]; and a limbic channel that projects from the medial orbitofrontal cortex, anterior cingulate cortex, amygdala, and the hippocampus to the ventral striatum, including the accumbens nucleus [58] (Figures 3 and 4).

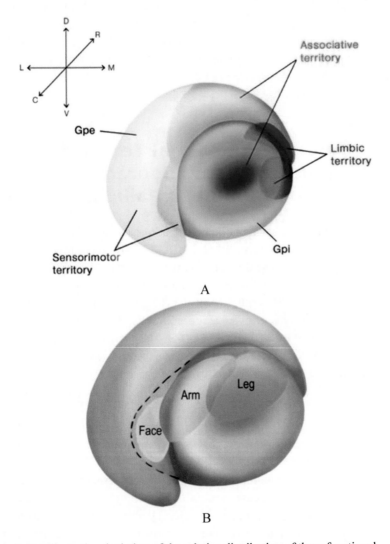

Figure 2. (A) Illustrative depiction of the relative distribution of three functional territories within the globus pallidus. (salmon-color = sensorimotor, green = associative, blue = limbic territory). M-L, R-C, and D-V axes represent the mediolateral, rostrocaudal, and dorsoventral planes, respectively. (B) Topographical organization of the sensorimotor territory in the GPi. (purple = leg, orange = arm, yellow = face).

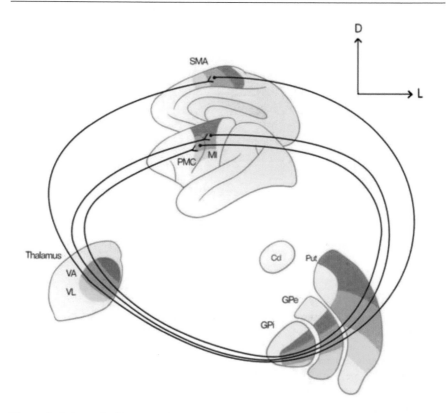

Figure 3. Schematic diagram of somatotopy in the motor loop through the basal ganglia. Segregated channels subserve sensorimotor processing along the cortico-striato-pallido-thalamo-cortical loop. Leg, arm, and face regions are somatotopically organized and interconnected from the supplementary motor area (SMA), premotor area (PMC), and primary motor area (MI), through putamen (Put), external (GPe), and internal (GPi) segments of the globus pallidus, subthalamic nucleus (STN), and thalamic nuclei (VA, VL). D, dorsal; L, lateral.

The sensorimotor territory of the GP receives input mainly from the postcommissural putamen and projects outflow predominantly toward the motor cortex via the VL nucleus of thalamus. The associative territory of the GP receives input from the head and body of the caudate nucleus and precommissural putamen [45], and outflow is directed toward the association cortex via the VA and MD nuclei of thalamus [31, 59-62].

The limbic territory of the GP predominantly receives input from ventral striatal areas [47, 63] and mainly directs output to the limbic cortex through the MD nucleus of thalamus [64].

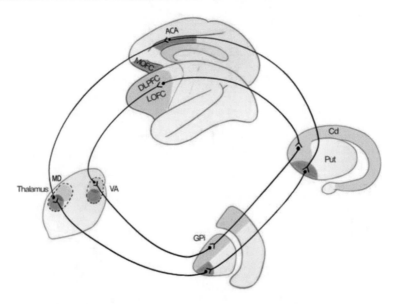

Figure 4. Schematic diagram of the associative and limbic loops. Green = associative territory; blue = limbic territory. ACA, anterior cingulate area; MOFC, medial orbitofacial cortex, DLPFC, dorsolateral prefrontal cortex; LOFC, lateral orbitofrontal cortex; Cd, caudate nucleus; Put, putamen; Gpe, external segment of globus pallidus; GPi, internal segment of globus pallidus; VA, ventroanterior nucleus of thalamus; MD, mediodorsal nucleus of thalamus.

Topographical Organization of the Sensorimotor Territory in the Globus Pallidus

Evidence of the somatotopical segregation of movement-related neurons has been found in the sensorimotor cortex, putamen, GPi, GPe, STN, and thalamus. Neuronal populations for the legs, arms and face remain discrete and interconnected throughout the various structures that comprise the motor circuit [65-68].

It has also been reported that specific regions within the GPi and GPe maintain this precise somatotopic organization [62, 67, 69]. Leg-, arm-, and face-related neurons are known to be located along the dorsoventral dimension. There is a similar leg-arm-face direction along the rostrocaudal dimension, in which the leg-related area is most anterior. However, somatotopic segregation seems to be mixed along the mediolateral dimension, with both arm- and face-related neurons tending to be more lateral than leg-related neurons. Overall, both the GPi and GPe seem to be characterized according to a topographically segregated body map that has three dimensions along the dorsoventral, rostrocaudal, and mediolateral axes (Figure 2B).In addition, the proximal limb regions (e.g., upper arm and thigh) tend to be more dorsal and medial compared with distal regions (e.g., wrist, hand, and finger) [34]. In conclusion, sensorimotor territory may be mostly located in the posteroventral region of the GPi, with a body map that is characterized as a mediodorsally located leg region compared with the arm and face region.

Topographical segregation of the input and output areas in the basal ganglia seems to be an essential feature required for physiological sensorimotor processing. Furthermore, enlargement of the receptive fields and consequent loss of specificity in pathological conditions has been reported [70-72]. The motor thalamus is the main target of pallidal output and receives somatotopically-organized information, which is mediated by segregated channels. These subcortical channels preserve a body map that is represented all the way along the various steps of the cortico-striato-pallido-thalamo-cortical loop (Figure 3) [62, 73, 74].

Clinical Aspects of Globus Pallidus Dysfunction

Dystonia

Dystonia is a movement disorder characterized by the co-contraction of agonist and antagonist muscles and involuntary, sustained, repetitive muscle contractions that lead to abnormal movements or postures. Patients are unable to control specific movements and suppress unwanted ones. Dystonia is caused by a heterogeneous group of diseases that probably have different pathophysiologic backgrounds, and there are no reliable animal models that can perfectly mimic the complex clinical features of dystonia. Therefore, the pathophysiology of dystonia is poorly understood compared with PD.

However, dystonia is generally thought to be caused by a dysfunctional basal ganglia/cortex network with abnormal plasticity, although some forms of dystonia may result from dysfunctions of other brain structures such as the cerebellum or cerebral cortex. The precise mechanisms responsible for abnormalities in the basal ganglia that could produce dystonia are not completely understood. However, a number of studies suggest that dystonia may be associated with a shift toward the direct pathway, which results from reduced activity along the putamen-GPe connection and the increased inhibition of STN and GPi by GPe efferents, thereby leading to excessive movement [75-79].

In a transgenic mouse model of dystonia that was used to investigate the effects of motor cortical stimulation on neuronal activity within the pallidum, it was reported that spontaneous activities with bursts and pauses in both the GPi and GPe are reduced and somatotopic organization in the GPi and GPe is disrupted [80]. Microinjections of Bic (antagonist of GABA-A receptors) into the posterior putamen (sensorimotor territory) induce dystonic movements in the neck of cats, mimicking spasmodic torticollis [81]. On the other hand, when Bic is directly injected into the GPi, hypertonic postures are induced in contralateral limbs [82]. In addition, microinjections into the sensorimotor territory of the GPe generate abnormal movements [3, 4]. Moreover, microinjections of muscimol, a GABAergic agonist, into the arm area of the GPi in monkeys induces focal dystonia that is characterized by the tonic and phasic coactivation of agonist and antagonist muscles in the arms and interference with reaching and grasping [8, 13]. Mink and Thach et al. suggested a hypothesis based on these results, specifically that GPi lesions may disrupt the ability to inhibit competing motor mechanisms in order to prevent interference with desired voluntary movements [9, 83].

Meanwhile, microinjection of Bic into the rostral (VL and VA nucleus) part of thalamus induces contralateral dystonic postures. Bic injection increases the discharge rate of thalamic neurons and decreases the threshold to evoke motor responses. Moreover, a large number of thalamic neurons respond to sensory inputs in a nonselective manner [84, 85]. These results suggest that hyperexcitability of the thalamo-cortical pathway play a role in dystonia [42]. At the level of cortex, the increase in the excitability of the supplementary motor area (SMA), which is thought to be the main cortical target of the basal ganglia projections that pass through the motor loop, was observed in a study on the 3-nitropropionic acid (3-NP) monkey model of limb dystonia. In addition, loss of selectivity in the receptive fields in the SMA proper has been reported [86]. A number of studies suggest that abnormalities in the cortical processing of somatosensory inputs may be the final common pathway linking various forms of dystonia [87].

Single-cell recordings of patients who have undergone functional neurosurgery demonstrate that the mean discharge rates in the GPi and GPe are reduced [10, 12, 88-91], though in some patients the firing rates are fairly similar to PD patients [5, 92]. However, the main features of dystonia can include other characteristics, such as burst-irregular neuronal activity and synchronization between pairs of GPi neurons [5-7, 10-12, 14]. Dystonic patients demonstrate a high number of cells that respond to passive and/or voluntary movements [6]. Excessive synchronization is associated with failure to elicit any movement, which might result from muscle rigidity due to the co-contraction of antagonistic muscles [6]. In animal experiments, GPi units demonstrate a regular discharge pattern [14, 93] intermixed with irregular bursts [66] that change into a highly irregular pattern and a profusion of bursts after treatment with 1-methyl-4-phenyl-1,2,3,6-tetrahydropyridine (MPTP) [14]. Interestingly, further reducing GPi output after pallidotomy improves, rather than worsens, dystonic movements and suggests that widening the receptive fields and increasing the tendency for group discharges may provide a more significant contribution to the pathophysiology of dystonia than the reduced mean firing rate [90, 92, 94]. The significance of these discharge patterns in dystonia has not been clarified. However, it is assumed that abnormal processing of somatosensory inputs transfer confusing signals to the cortex and this could present as the dystonic features.

Thalamotomy [95] and pallidotomy [96] are typically applied only to extreme cases, but their side effects discourage routine use and, unfortunately, pharmacological therapies are usually ineffective. Thus, as a new treatment strategy, DBS has been used to treat dystonia following successfully being used to treat PD [97-99]. In particular, because GPi-DBS relieves levodopa-induced dyskinesia in PD patients [100], GPi has been a main target for the treatment of dystonia. The therapeutic mechanism of DBS in dystonia may be the disruption of "noisy signal" and allowing motor programs to be gated with ease. Multiple open-label studies demonstrate that GPi-DBS is highly effective for the treatment of dystonia and is well tolerated [5, 7, 11, 12, 101].

Nowadays, the pathophysiology and the explanation of various electrical findings of GP in dystonia remain diverse and unclear. However, clinical treatment has been developed gradually including DBS. Animal experiments, especially research on primates, are needed to evaluate the pathology based on anatomofunctional relation.

Attention Deficit Hyperactivity Disorder (ADHD)

According to animal studies performed on primates to determine the anatomofunctional circuits of the basal ganglia, attention deficit is elicited after the microinjection of Bic into the anteromedial area of GPe, which is characterized by a moderate staining of calbindin (Cb) immunoreactivity and it corresponds to the associative territory [4]. These regions reportedly receive striatal inputs from the most posterior part of the associative territory, and from the most anterior part of the sensorimotor territory [26, 29, 30, 33, 48], and more specifically from striatal regions linked to the supplementary motor area [59]. The efferent axonal fibers from the part of GPe are found in the lateral part anteriorly and in the dorsal part posteriorly within the GPi. The neurons in these regions are known to project to the associative prefrontal cortex via the thalamus, as well as to the supplementary and pre-supplementary motor cortices [61, 74]. These results indicate that the attention deficit circuit is involved in the subregions of the basal ganglia that are linked to the cortical areas, which play a major role in both motor planning and attention processes.

Comparatively, hyperactivity with attention deficit circuit appears to involve roughly the same portions of the striatum, but labelling is slightly more ventrally located in the putamen and does not reach the caudate nucleus [4]. This striatal zone not only receives cortical projections from the most anterior part of the secondary motor areas, such as the supplementary motor cortex, but also from the rostral cingulate motor cortex, which are implicated not only in the execution of the movements but also in higher-order cognitive aspects of movement such as motor selection and error detection [102-104]. The efferent axonal fibers from the part of GPe occupy the anterior and more ventral portions of the sensorimotor territory within the GPi [104]. Moreover, functional imaging studies (PET or functional MRI) on patients with ADHD indicate reduced metabolism in the prefrontal cortical areas [105, 106], the anterior cingulate cortex [107], associative striatum [108-112], and pallidum [109, 113]. Based on these findings, it has been suggested that ADHD as a whole represents a deficiency in the parts of the basal ganglia that are linked to the associative prefrontal cortex and the secondary motor cortices involved in attention processes and motor planning.

Tics/Obsessive-Compulsive Disorder (OCD)

Tics, which are a component of Tourette's syndrome (TS), are characterized as brief, sudden, repetitive stereotyped movements (motor tics) or sounds (vocal tics), which can be either simple or complex [114-117]. Based on the pathophysiology of the movement disorders associated with basal ganglia dysfunction, tics are described as hyperkinetic movement disorders that presumably result from a reduction in the normal inhibitory output of the basal ganglia [41, 42], which in turn disinhibits motor areas and results in unwanted movement [118, 119]. Reduced volumes and abnormal asymmetries in the caudate, putamen, and GP have been described in patients with TS [35, 120-124]. In addition, a postmortem study of patients with TS reported an imbalance in the distribution of inhibitory neurons in the striatum and GPi, suggesting that the cortico-striato-pallido-thalamic circuitry is fundamentally altered in patients with TS [125].

In a primate model [4], stereotyped behaviors were noted after Bic microinjections into the anterior and medioventral portion of the GPe, which appear to be densely stained with Cb and correspond to the limbic territory. The stereotyped behaviors resembled the tics and compulsive disorders described in patients with TS or OCD. The striatal region, which was retrogradely labelled by the injection of an axonal tracer into the region of the GPe, is a ventromedial striatal area that is located at the border between the dorsal portion of the nucleus accumbens and the ventral part of the head of the caudate nucleus. Nucleus accumbens is the major structure that receives limbic inputs from the orbitofrontal, anterior cingulate and insular cortices [58, 126-128], amygdala and hippocampus [129-131] - all of which process emotional and motivational information. The anterogradely labelled GPe fibers, originating from stereotypy-related sites, occupy the anterior and ventromedial regions of the GPi, but most of all the SNr. Labelled terminal axons have also been observed in the STN, but they are restricted to the most anteromedial part. These regions of the output structures of the basal ganglia project to the orbitofrontal cortex via the medial part of the thalamus [132, 133]. Moreover, another particular output target of the ventral limbic GPe is the dopaminergic neurons of the SNc [132, 134], which are considered to play a major role in focusing attention and rewarding stimuli [135]. These results indicate that the pallidum could be involved in OCD. It was also reported that bilateral lesions in GP produce striking OCD-like behaviors [136, 137].

The involvement of the GPi in patients with tics is supported by imaging studies that report reduced basal ganglia nuclei volumes in these patients [120, 121, 138] and reduced neuronal activity in GPi [118, 119, 122], which presumably lead to increased activity in the inhibitory direct pathway and decreased activity in the indirect pathway. The net effect of these changes is to reduce the firing rate of the inhibitory neurons in GPi, which leads to less inhibition of the thalamus. Subsequently, the emergence of unwanted stereotyped movement, such as tics, results from the disinhibition of motor areas [118, 119].

According to DBS studies [139-141], patients with medically intractable TS who underwent DBS of the centromedian-parafascicular complex (CM-Pf) in the thalamus or the GPi demonstrate significant clinical improvement. The CM-Pf is reciprocally connected to the basal ganglia, giving rise to a projection to the striatum and receiving inputs from the GPi [142]. In addition, it was reported that tic severity is markedly improved in TS patients following unilateral pallidotomy [35]. These studies indicate that GPi is most likely a component of the pathological neural network that evokes tics.

Clinical Pearls

1. The GP is an important output structure in the cortico-basal ganglia-thalamo-cortical circuit and participates in diverse movements and behavioral adjustment. According to recently published studies, anatomofunctional segregation is the dominant characteristic of GP and could be a useful target in research on functional networks around the basal ganglia.

2. Comprehensive knowledge of functional anatomy and the roles of the GP will be useful for clinicians to understand not only the pathophysiology of movement disorders but also behavioral disorders such as ADHD and OCD. Furthermore, additional research will facilitate the development of precise therapeutic targets for these disorders, enhance the efficacy of surgical intervention, and help avoid adverse effects.

Disclosure

The authors confirm that they have no financial arrangements to disclose.

References

[1]   Lang AE, Lozano AM. Parkinson's disease. Second of two parts. *N Engl J Med.* 1998;339:1130-1143.

[2]   Delong MR, Georgopoulos AP, Crutcher MD, Mitchell SJ, Richardson RT, Alexander GE. Functional organization of the basal ganglia: contributions of single-cell recording studies. *Ciba Found Symp*. 1984;107:64-82.

[3]   Grabli D, McCairn K, Hirsch EC, Agid Y, Feger J, Francois C, et al. Behavioural disorders induced by external globus pallidus dysfunction in primates: I. Behavioural study. *Brain*. 2004;127:2039-2054.

[4]   Francois C, Grabli D, McCairn K, Jan C, Karachi C, Hirsch EC, et al. Behavioural disorders induced by external globus pallidus dysfunction in primates II. Anatomical study. *Brain*. 2004;127:2055-2070.

[5]   Hutchison WD, Lang AE, Dostrovsky JO, Lozano AM. Pallidal neuronal activity: implications for models of dystonia. *Ann Neurol*. 2003;53:480-488.

[6]   Magarinos-Ascone CM, Regidor I, Gomez-Galan M, Cabanes-Martinez L, Figueiras-Mendez R. Deep brain stimulation in the globus pallidus to treat dystonia: electrophysiological characteristics and 2 years' follow-up in 10 patients. *Neuroscience*. 2008;152:558-571.

[7]   Magarinos-Ascone CM, Regidor I, Martinez-Castrillo JC, Gomez-Galan M, Figueiras-Mendez R. Pallidal stimulation relieves myoclonus-dystonia syndrome. *Journal of Neurology Neurosurgery and Psychiatry*. 2005;76:989-991.

[8]   Mink JW, Thach WT. Basal ganglia motor control.3. Pallidal ablation - normal reaction-time, muscle cocontraction, and slow movement. *J Neurophysiol*. 1991;65:330-351.

[9]   Mink JW, Thach WT. Basal ganglia intrinsic circuits and their role in behavior. *Curr Opin Neurobiol*. 1993;3:950-957.

[10] Starr PA, Rau GM, Davis V, Marks WJ, Ostrem JL, Simmons D, et al. Spontaneous pallidal neuronal activity in human dystonia: Comparison with Parkinson's disease and normal macaque. *J Neurophysiol*. 2005;93:3165-3176.

[11] Steigerwald F, Hinz L, Pinsker MO, Herzog J, Stiller RU, Kopper F, et al. Effect of propofol anesthesia on pallidal neuronal discharges in generalized dystonia. *Neurosci Lett*. 2005;386:156-159.

[12] Vitek JL, Chockkan V, Zhang JY, Kaneoke Y, Evatt M, DeLong MR, et al. Neuronal activity in the basal ganglia in patients with generalized dystonia and hemiballismus. *Ann Neurol*. 1999;46:22-35.

[13] Wenger KK, Musch KL, Mink JW. Impaired reaching and grasping after focal inactivation of globus pallidus pars interna in the monkey. *J Neurophysiol*. 1999;82:2049-2060.

[14] Wichmann T, Bergman H, Starr PA, Subramanian T, Watts RL, DeLong MR. Comparison of MPTP-induced changes in spontaneous neuronal discharge in the internal pallidal segment and in the substantia nigra pars reticulata in primates. *Exp Brain Res*. 1999;125:397-409.

[15] Ardouin C, Pillon B, Peiffer E, Bejjani P, Limousin P, Damier P, et al. Bilateral subthalamic or pallidal stimulation for Parkinson's disease affects neither memory nor executive functions: A consecutive series of 62 patients. *Ann Neurol*. 1999;46:217-223.

[16] Dujardin K, Krystkowiak P, Defebvre L, Blond S, Destee A. A case of severe dysexecutive syndrome consecutive to chronic bilateral pallidal stimulation. *Neuropsychologia*. 2000;38:1305-1315.

[17] Lang AE, Lozano AM, Montgomery E, Duff J, Tasker R, Hutchinson W. Posteroventral medial pallidotomy in advanced Parkinson's disease. *N Engl J Med*. 1997;337:1036-1042.

[18] Miyawaki E, Perlmutter JS, Troster AI, Videen TO, Koller WC. The behavioral complications of pallidal stimulation: A case report. *Brain Cogn*. 2000;42:417-434.

[19] Roane DM, Yu M, Feinberg TE, Rogers JD. Hypersexuality after pallidal surgery in Parkinson disease. *Neuropsychiatry Neuropsychol Behav Neurol*. 2002;15:247-251.

[20] Alexander GE, DeLong MR, Strick PL. Parallel organization of functionally segregated circuits linking basal ganglia and cortex. *Annu Rev Neurosci*. 1986;9:357-381.

[21] Brown J, Bullock D, Grossberg S. How the basal ganglia use parallel excitatory and inhibitory learning pathways to selectively respond to unexpected rewarding cues. *J Neurosci*. 1999;19:10502-10511.

[22] Knowlton BJ, Mangels JA, Squire LR. A neostriatal habit learning system in humans. *Science*. 1996;273:1399-1402.

[23] Nakano K. Neural circuits and topographic organization of the basal ganglia and related regions. *Brain Dev*. 2000;22 Suppl 1:S5-16.

[24] Rolls ET. Neurophysiology and cognitive functions of the striatum. *Rev Neurol (Paris)*. 1994;150:648-660.

[25] Schultz W, Dayan P, Montague PR. A neural substrate of prediction and reward. *Science*. 1997;275:1593-1599.

[26] Francois C, Yelnik J, Percheron G, Fenelon G. Topographic distribution of the axonal endings from the sensorimotor and associative striatum in the macaque pallidum and substantia nigra. *Exp Brain Res*. 1994;102:305-318.

[27] Haber SN, Fudge JL, McFarland NR. Striatonigrostriatal pathways in primates form an ascending spiral from the shell to the dorsolateral striatum. *J Neurosci.* 2000;20:2369-2382.

[28] Haber SN, Lynd E, Klein C, Groenewegen HJ. Topographic organization of the ventral striatal efferent projections in the rhesus monkey: an anterograde tracing study. *J Comp Neurol.* 1990;293:282-298.

[29] Hedreen JC, DeLong MR. Organization of striatopallidal, striatonigral, and nigrostriatal projections in the macaque. *J Comp Neurol.* 1991;304:569-595.

[30] Parent A, Bouchard C, Smith Y. The striatopallidal and striatonigral projections: two distinct fiber systems in primate. *Brain Res.* 1984;303:385-390.

[31] Parent A, Hazrati LN. Functional anatomy of the basal ganglia. II. The place of subthalamic nucleus and external pallidum in basal ganglia circuitry. *Brain Res Brain Res Rev.* 1995;20:128-154.

[32] Saint-Cyr JA, Ungerleider LG, Desimone R. Organization of visual cortical inputs to the striatum and subsequent outputs to the pallido-nigral complex in the monkey. *J Comp Neurol.* 1990;298:129-156.

[33] Smith Y, Parent A. Differential connections of caudate nucleus and putamen in the squirrel monkey (Saimiri sciureus). *Neuroscience.* 1986;18:347-371.

[34] Baker KB, Lee JY, Mavinkurve G, Russo GS, Walter B, DeLong MR, et al. Somatotopic organization in the internal segment of the globus pallidus in Parkinson's disease. *Exp Neurol.* 2010;222:219-225.

[35] Zhuang P, Hallett M, Zhang X, Li J, Zhang Y, Li Y. Neuronal activity in the globus pallidus internus in patients with tics. *J Neurol Neurosurg Psychiatry.* 2009;80:1075-1081.

[36] Donaldson IM, Marsden CD, Schneide SA, Bhatia KP. Structure and function of the basal ganglia. Marsden's book of movement disorders. United States: Oxford University Press; 2012.

[37] Haber SN, Kunishio K, Mizobuchi M, Lynd-Balta E. The orbital and medial prefrontal circuit through the primate basal ganglia. *J Neurosci.* 1995;15:4851-4867.

[38] Selemon LD, Goldman-Rakic PS. Longitudinal topography and interdigitation of corticostriatal projections in the rhesus monkey. *J Neurosci.* 1985;5:776-794.

[39] Alexander GE, Crutcher MD, DeLong MR. Basal ganglia-thalamocortical circuits: parallel substrates for motor, oculomotor, "prefrontal" and "limbic" functions. *Prog. Brain Res.* 1990;85:119-146.

[40] Holsapple JW, Preston JB, Strick PL. The origin of thalamic inputs to the "hand" representation in the primary motor cortex. *J Neurosci.* 1991;11:2644-2654.

[41] Albin RL, Young AB, Penney JB. The functional-anatomy of basal ganglia disorders. *Trends Neurosci.* 1989;12:366-375.

[42] DeLong MR. Primate models of movement disorders of basal ganglia origin. *Trends Neurosci.* 1990;13:281-285.

[43] Herrero MT, Barcia C, Navarro JM. Functional anatomy of thalamus and basal ganglia. *Childs Nerv Syst.* 2002;18:386-404.

[44] Alexander GE, Crutcher MD. Functional architecture of basal ganglia circuits: neural substrates of parallel processing. *Trends Neurosci.* 1990;13:266-271.

[45] Shink E, Sidibe M, Smith Y. Efferent connections of the internal globus pallidus in the squirrel monkey: II. Topography and synaptic organization of pallidal efferents to the pedunculopontine nucleus. *J Comp Neurol.* 1997;382:348-363.

[46] Parent A, Sato F, Wu Y, Gauthier J, Levesque M, Parent M. Organization of the basal ganglia: the importance of axonal collateralization. *Trends Neurosci.* 2000;23:S20-27.

[47] Nakano K, Kayahara T, Tsutsumi T, Ushiro H. Neural circuits and functional organization of the striatum. *J Neurol.* 2000;247 Suppl 5:V1-15.

[48] Hazrati LN, Parent A. The striatopallidal projection displays a high degree of anatomical specificity in the primate. *Brain Res.* 1992;592:213-227.

[49] Selemon LD, Goldman-Rakic PS. Topographic intermingling of striatonigral and striatopallidal neurons in the rhesus monkey. *J Comp Neurol.* 1990;297:359-376.

[50] Parent A, Hazrati LN. Functional anatomy of the basal ganglia. I. The cortico-basal ganglia-thalamo-cortical loop. *Brain Res Brain Res Rev.* 1995;20:91-127.

[51] Joel D, Weiner I. The connections of the primate subthalamic nucleus: indirect pathways and the open-interconnected scheme of basal ganglia-thalamocortical circuitry. *Brain Res Brain Res Rev.* 1997;23:62-78.

[52] Wichmann T, DeLong MR. Pathophysiology of Parkinson's disease: the MPTP primate model of the human disorder. *Ann N Y Acad Sci.* 2003;991:199-213.

[53] Flaherty AW, Graybiel AM. Corticostriatal transformations in the primate somatosensory system. Projections from physiologically mapped body-part representations. *J Neurophysiol.* 1991;66:1249-1263.

[54] Kunzle H. Bilateral projections from precentral motor cortex to the putamen and other parts of the basal ganglia. An autoradiographic study in Macaca fascicularis. *Brain Res.* 1975;88:195-209.

[55] Yeterian EH, Pandya DN. Prefrontostriatal connections in relation to cortical architectonic organization in rhesus monkeys. *J Comp Neurol.* 1991;312:43-67.

[56] Yeterian EH, Pandya DN. Striatal connections of the parietal association cortices in rhesus monkeys. *J Comp Neurol.* 1993;332:175-197.

[57] Yeterian EH, Pandya DN. Corticostriatal connections of the superior temporal region in rhesus monkeys. *J Comp Neurol.* 1998;399:384-402.

[58] Haber SN, Kunishio K, Mizobuchi M, Lyndbalta E. The Orbital and Medial Prefrontal Circuit through the Primate Basal Ganglia. *J Neurosci.* 1995;15:4851-4867.

[59] Kaneda K, Nambu A, Tokuno H, Takada M. Differential processing patterns of motor information via striatopallidal and striatonigral projections. *J Neurophysiol.* 2002;88:1420-1432.

[60] Middleton FA, Strick PL. Anatomical evidence for cerebellar and basal ganglia involvement in higher cognitive function. *Science.* 1994;266:458-461.

[61] Middleton FA, Strick PL. Basal-ganglia 'projections' to the prefrontal cortex of the primate. *Cereb Cortex.* 2002;12:926-935.

[62] Middleton FA, Strick PL. Basal ganglia and cerebellar loops: motor and cognitive circuits. *Brain Res Brain Res Rev.* 2000;31:236-250.

[63] Gerfen CR. The neostriatal mosaic: compartmentalization of corticostriatal input and striatonigral output systems. *Nature.* 1984;311:461-464.

[64] Bolam JP, Hanley JJ, Booth PAC, Bevan MD. Synaptic organisation of the basal ganglia. *J Anat.* 2000;196:527-542.

[65] Takada M, Tokuno H, Nambu A, Inase M. Corticostriatal projections from the somatic motor areas of the frontal cortex in the macaque monkey: segregation versus overlap of input zones from the primary motor cortex, the supplementary motor area, and the premotor cortex. *Exp Brain Res.* 1998;120:114-128.

[66] DeLong MR. Activity of pallidal neurons during movement. *J Neurophysiol.* 1971;34:414-427.

[67] DeLong MR, Crutcher MD, Georgopoulos AP. Primate globus pallidus and subthalamic nucleus: functional organization. *J Neurophysiol.* 1985;53:530-543.

[68] Vitek JL, Ashe J, DeLong MR, Alexander GE. Physiologic properties and somatotopic organization of the primate motor thalamus. *J Neurophysiol.* 1994;71:1498-1513.

[69] Vitek JL, Bakay RA, DeLong MR. Microelectrode-guided pallidotomy for medically intractable Parkinson's disease. *Adv Neurol.* 1997;74:183-198.

[70] Filion M, Tremblay L, Bedard PJ. Abnormal influences of passive limb movement on the activity of globus pallidus neurons in parkinsonian monkeys. *Brain Res.* 1988;444:165-176.

[71] Romanelli P, Heit G, Hill BC, Kraus A, Hastie T, Bronte-Stewart HM. Microelectrode recording revealing a somatotopic body map in the subthalamic nucleus in humans with Parkinson disease. *J Neurosurg.* 2004;100:611-618.

[72] Vitek JL, Bakay RA, Hashimoto T, Kaneoke Y, Mewes K, Zhang JY, et al. Microelectrode-guided pallidotomy: technical approach and its application in medically intractable Parkinson's disease. *J Neurosurg.* 1998;88:1027-1043.

[73] Hoover JE, Strick PL. Multiple output channels in the basal ganglia. *Science.* 1993;259:819-821.

[74] Middleton FA, Strick PL. Basal ganglia output and cognition: evidence from anatomical, behavioral, and clinical studies. *Brain Cogn.* 2000;42:183-200.

[75] Casey DE. Dopamine D1 (SCH 23390) and D2 (haloperidol) antagonists in drug-naive monkeys. *Psychopharmacology (Berl).* 1992;107:18-22.

[76] Hallett M. Dystonia: abnormal movements result from loss of inhibition. *Adv Neurol.* 2004;94:1-9.

[77] Hallett M. Pathophysiology of writer's cramp. *Hum Mov Sci.* 2006;25:454-463.

[78] Hantraye P, Riche D, Maziere M, Isacson O. A primate model of Huntington's disease: behavioral and anatomical studies of unilateral excitotoxic lesions of the caudate-putamen in the baboon. *Exp Neurol.* 1990;108:91-104.

[79] Mitchell IJ, Luquin R, Boyce S, Clarke CE, Robertson RG, Sambrook MA, et al. Neural mechanisms of dystonia: evidence from a 2-

deoxyglucose uptake study in a primate model of dopamine agonist-induced dystonia. *Mov Disord.* 1990;5:49-54.

[80] Chiken S, Shashidharan P, Nambu A. Cortically evoked long-lasting inhibition of pallidal neurons in a transgenic mouse model of dystonia. *J Neurosci.* 2008;28:13967-13977.

[81] Yamada H, Fujimoto KI, Yoshida M. Neuronal mechanism underlying dystonia induced by bicuculline injection into the putamen of the cat. *Brain Res.* 1995;677:333-336.

[82] Burbaud P, Bonnet B, Guehl D, Lagueny A, Bioulac B. Movement disorders induced by gamma-aminobutyric agonist and antagonist injections into the internal lobus pallidus and substantia nigra pars reticulata of the monkey. *Brain Res.* 1998;780:102-107.

[83] Guehl D, Cuny E, Ghorayeb I, Michelet T, Bioulac B, Burbaud P. Primate models of dystonia. *Prog Neurobiol.* 2009;87:118-131.

[84] Guehl D, Burbaud P, Boraud T, Bioulac B. Bicuculline injections into the rostral and caudal motor thalamus of the monkey induce different types of dystonia. *Eur J Neurosci.* 2000;12:1033-1037.

[85] Macia F, Escola L, Guehl D, Michelet T, Bioulac B, Burbaud P. Neuronal activity in the monkey motor thalamus during bicuculline-induced dystonia. *Eur J Neurosci.* 2002;15:1353-1362.

[86] Cuny E, Ghorayeb I, Guehl D, Escola L, Bioulac B, Burbaud P. Sensory motor mismatch within the supplementary motor area in the dystonic monkey. *Neurobiol Dis.* 2008;30:151-161.

[87] Vidailhet M, Grabli D, Roze E. Pathophysiology of dystonia. *Curr Opin Neurol.* 2009;22:406-413.

[88] Lenz FA, Suarez JI, Metman LV, Reich SG, Karp BI, Hallett M, et al. Pallidal activity during dystonia: somatosensory reorganisation and changes with severity. *J Neurol Neurosurg Psychiatry.* 1998;65:767-770.

[89] Tang JKH, Moro E, Mahant N, Hutchison WD, Lang AE, Lozano AM, et al. Neuronal firing rates and patterns in the globus pallidus internus of patients with cervical dystonia differ from those with Parkinson's disease. *J Neurophysiol.* 2007;98:720-729.

[90] Vitek JL. Pathophysiology of dystonia: A neuronal model. *Mov Disord.* 2002;17:S49-S62.

[91] Zhuang P, Li YJ, Hallett M. Neuronal activity in the basal ganglia and thalamus in patients with dystonia. *Clin Neurophysiol.* 2004;115:2542-2557.

[92] Schrock LE, Ostrem JL, Turner RS, Shimamoto SA, Starr PA. The
      subthalamic nucleus in primary dystonia: Single-unit discharge
      characteristics. *J Neurophysiol*. 2009;102:3740-3752.

[93] Gernert M, Bennay M, Fedrowitz M, Rehders JH, Richter A. Altered
      discharge pattern of basal ganglia output neurons in an animal model of
      idiopathic dystonia. *J Neurosci*. 2002;22:7244-7253.

[94] Starr PA, Marks WJ, Rau G, Lindsey N, Simmons D, Turner RS.
      Spontaneous pallidal discharge in 15 cases of dystonia: Comparison with
      Parkinson's disease and normal Macaque. *Mov Disord*. 2004;19:S90-
      S90.

[95] Andrew J, Fowler CJ, Harrison MJ. Stereotaxic thalamotomy in 55 cases
      of dystonia. *Brain*. 1983;106 (Pt 4):981-1000.

[96] Vitek JL, Zhang J, Evatt M, Mewes K, DeLong MR, Hashimoto T, et al.
      GPi pallidotomy for dystonia: clinical outcome and neuronal activity.
      Adv Neurol. 1998;78:211-219.

[97] Limousin P, Krack P, Pollak P, Benazzouz A, Ardouin C, Hoffmann D,
      et al. Electrical stimulation of the subthalamic nucleus in advanced
      Parkinson's disease. *N Engl J Med*. 1998;339:1105-1111.

[98] Magarinos-Ascone CM, Figueiras-Mendez R, Riva-Meana C, Cordoba-
      Fernandez A. Subthalamic neuron activity related to tremor and
      movement in Parkinson's disease. *Eur J Neurosci*. 2000;12:2597-2607.

[99] Rodriguez-Oroz MC, Rodriguez M, Guridi J, Mewes K, Chockkman V,
      Vitek J, et al. The subthalamic nucleus in Parkinson's disease:
      somatotopic organization and physiological characteristics. *Brain*.
      2001;124:1777-1790.

[100] Jankovic J, Lai E, Ben-Arie L, Krauss JK, Grossman R. Levodopa-
      induced dyskinesias treated by pallidotomy. *J Neurol Sci*. 1999;167:62-
      67.

[101] Coubes P, Roubertie A, Vayssiere N, Hemm S, Echenne B. Treatment of
      DYT1-generalised dystonia by stimulation of the internal globus
      pallidus. *Lancet*. 2000;355:2220-2221.

[102] Akkal D, Bioulac B, Audin J, Burbaud P. Comparison of neuronal
      activity in the rostral supplementary and cingulate motor areas during a
      task with cognitive and motor demands. *Eur J Neurosci*. 2002;15:887-
      904.

[103] Isomura Y, Ito Y, Akazawa T, Nambu A, Takada M. Neural coding of
      "attention for action" and "response selection" in primate anterior
      cingulate cortex. *J Neurosci*. 2003;23:8002-8012.

[104] Takada M, Tokuno H, Hamada I, Inase M, Ito Y, Imanishi M, et al. Organization of inputs from cingulate motor areas to basal ganglia in macaque monkey. *Eur J Neurosci.* 2001;14:1633-1650.

[105] Amen DG, Paldi JH, Thisted RA. Brain Spect Imaging. *J Am Acad Child Adolesc Psychiatry.* 1993;32:1080-1081.

[106] Spalletta G, Pasini A, Pau F, Guido G, Menghini L, Caltagirone C. Prefrontal blood flow dysregulation in drug naive ADHD children without structural abnormalities. *J Neural Transm.* 2001;108:1203-1216.

[107] Bush G, Frazier JA, Rauch SL, Seidman LJ, Whalen PJ, Jenike MA, et al. Anterior cingulate cortex dysfunction in attention-deficit/hyperactivity disorder revealed by fMRI and the Counting Stroop. *Biol Psychiatry.* 1999;45:1542-1552.

[108] Castellanos FX. Neural substrates of attention-deficit hyperactivity disorder. *Adv Neurol.* 2001;85:197-206.

[109] Castellanos FX, Giedd JN, Marsh WL, Hamburger SD, Vaituzis AC, Dickstein DP, et al. Quantitative brain magnetic resonance imaging in attention-deficit hyperactivity disorder. *Arch Gen Psychiatry.* 1996;53:607-616.

[110] Filipek PA, Semrud-Clikeman M, Steingard RJ, Renshaw PF, Kennedy DN, Biederman J. Volumetric MRI analysis comparing subjects having attention-deficit hyperactivity disorder with normal controls. *Neurology.* 1997;48:589-601.

[111] Teicher MH, Anderson CM, Polcari A, Glod CA, Maas LC, Renshaw PF. Functional deficits in basal ganglia of children with attention-deficit/hyperactivity disorder shown with functional magnetic resonance imaging relaxometry. *Nat Med.* 2000;6:470-473.

[112] Vaidya CJ, Austin G, Kirkorian G, Ridlehuber HW, Desmond JE, Glover GH, et al. Selective effects of methylphenidate in attention deficit hyperactivity disorder: A functional magnetic resonance study. *Proc Natl Acad Sci U S A.* 1998;95:14494-14499.

[113] Aylward EH, Reiss AL, Reader MJ, Singer HS, Brown JE, Denckla MB. Basal ganglia volumes in children with attention-deficit hyperactivity disorder. *J Child Neurol.* 1996;11:112-115.

[114] Cohen AJ, Leckman JF. Sensory phenomena associated with gilles-de-la-tourettes syndrome. *J Clin Psychiatry.* 1992;53:319-323.

[115] Pauls DL, Alsobrook JP, 2nd, Goodman W, Rasmussen S, Leckman JF. A family study of obsessive-compulsive disorder. *Am J Psychiatry.* 1995;152:76-84.

[116] Pauls DL, Raymond CL, Stevenson JM, Leckman JF. A family study of Gilles de la Tourette syndrome. *Am J Hum Genet.* 1991;48:154-163.

[117] Walkup JT, LaBuda MC, Singer HS, Brown J, Riddle MA, Hurko O. Family study and segregation analysis of Tourette syndrome: evidence for a mixed model of inheritance. *Am J Hum Genet.* 1996;59:684-693.

[118] Mink JW. Basal ganglia dysfunction in Tourette's syndrome: A new hypothesis. *Pediatr Neurol.* 2001;25:190-198.

[119] Mink JW. The Basal Ganglia and involuntary movements: impaired inhibition of competing motor patterns. *Arch Neurol.* 2003;60:1365-1368.

[120] Bloch MH, Leckman JF, Zhu HT, Peterson BS. Caudate volumes in childhood predict symptom severity in adults with Tourette syndrome. *Neurology.* 2005;65:1253-1258.

[121] Eidelberg D, Moeller JR, Antonini A, Kazumata K, Dhawan V, Budman C, et al. The metabolic anatomy of Tourette's syndrome. *Neurology.* 1997;48:927-934.

[122] Peterson BS, Skudlarski P, Anderson AW, Zhang H, Gatenby JC, Lacadie CM, et al. A functional magnetic resonance imaging study of tic suppression in Tourette syndrome. *Arch Gen Psychiatry.* 1998;55:326-333.

[123] Peterson BS, Thomas P, Kane MJ, Scahill L, Zhang H, Bronen R, et al. Basal Ganglia volumes in patients with Gilles de la Tourette syndrome. *Arch Gen Psychiatry.* 2003;60:415-424.

[124] Singer HS, Reiss AL, Brown JE, Aylward EH, Shih B, Chee E, et al. Volumetric MRI changes in basal ganglia of children with Tourettes-syndrome. *Neurology.* 1993;43:A409-A409.

[125] Kalanithi PSA, Zheng W, Kataoka Y, DiFiglia M, Grantz H, Saper CB, et al. Altered parvalbumin-positive neuron distribution in basal ganglia of individuals with Tourette syndrome. *Proc Natl Acad Sci U S A.* 2005;102:13307-13312.

[126] Chikama M, McFarland NR, Amaral DG, Haber SN. Insular cortical projections to functional regions of the striatum correlate with cortical cytoarchitectonic organization in the primate. *J Neurosci.* 1997;17:9686-9705.

[127] Ferry AT, Ongur D, An XH, Price JL. Prefrontal cortical projections to the striatum in macaque monkeys: Evidence for an organization related to prefrontal networks. *J Comp Neurol.* 2000;425:447-470.

[128] Kunishio K, Haber SN. Primate cingulostriatal projection - limbic striatal versus sensorimotor striatal input. *J Comp Neurol*. 1994;350:337-356.

[129] Friedman DP, Aggleton JP, Saunders RC. Comparison of hippocampal, amygdala, and perirhinal projections to the nucleus accumbens: Combined anterograde and retrograde tracing study in the macaque brain. *J Comp Neurol*. 2002;450:345-365.

[130] Fudge JL, Haber SN. Defining the caudal ventral striatum in primates: Cellular and histochemical features. *J Neurosci*. 2002;22:10078-10082.

[131] Russchen FT, Bakst I, Amaral DG, Price JL. The amygdalostriatal projections in the monkey - an anterograde tracing study. *Brain Res*. 1985;329:241-257.

[132] Haber SN, Lyndbalta E, Mitchell SJ. The organization of the descending ventral pallidal projections in the monkey. *J Comp Neurol*. 1993;329:111-128.

[133] Ilinsky IA, Jouandet ML, Goldmanrakic PS. Organization of the nigrothalamocortical system in the rhesus-monkey. *J Comp Neurol*. 1985;236:315-330.

[134] Gerfen CR. The neostriatal mosaic - multiple levels of compartmental organization. *Trends Neurosci*. 1992;15:133-139.

[135] Schultz W. Dopamine neurons and their role in reward mechanisms. *Curr Opin Neurobiol*. 1997;7:191-197.

[136] Laplane D, Baulac M, Widlocher D, Dubois B. Pure psychic akinesia with bilateral lesions of basal ganglia. *J Neurol Neurosurg Psychiatry*. 1984;47:377-385.

[137] Laplane D, Levasseur M, Pillon B, Dubois B, Baulac M, Mazoyer B, et al. Obsessive-compulsive and other behavioral-changes with bilateral basal ganglia lesions - a neuropsychological, magnetic-resonance imaging and positron tomography study. *Brain*. 1989;112:699-725.

[138] Singer HS, Reiss AL, Brown JE, Aylward EH, Shih B, Chee E, et al. Volumetric MRI changes in basal ganglia of children with Tourette's syndrome. *Neurology*. 1993;43:950-956.

[139] Ackermans L, Temel Y, Cath D, van der Linden C, Bruggeman R, Kleijer M, et al. Deep brain stimulation in Tourette's syndrome: two targets? *Mov Disord*. 2006;21:709-713.

[140] Diederich NJ, Kalteis K, Stamenkovic M, Pieri V, Alesch F. Efficient internal pallidal stimulation in Gilles de la Tourette syndrome: a case report. *Mov Disord*. 2005;20:1496-1499.

[141] Houeto JL, Karachi C, Mallet L, Pillon B, Yelnik J, Mesnage V, et al. Tourette's syndrome and deep brain stimulation. *J Neurol Neurosurg Psychiatry*. 2005;76:992-995.

[142] Sadikot AF, Parent A, Francois C. Efferent connections of the centromedian and parafascicular thalamic nuclei in the squirrel-monkey - a pha-l study of subcortical projections. *J Comp Neurol*. 1992;315:137-159.

In: Globus Pallidus   ISBN: 978-1-62948-367-2
Editors: C.R. Gordon, T.G. Abbadelli © 2013 Nova Science Publishers, Inc.

Chapter 3

A Population Activity Model of Cortico-Striatal Circuitry Underlying Behavioral Inhibition in Rats

Kiah Hardcastle, Gregory D. Smith[1] and Joshua A. Burk[2]*
[1]Departments of Applied Science
[2]Department Psychology
The College of William & Mary, Williamsburg, Virginia, US

Abstract

A failure of response inhibition is thought to contribute to several psychological disorders. Response inhibition can be assessed with tasks that require the ability to stop an initiated response, such as the stop signal reaction time task. Numerous studies have shown that the basal ganglia are critical for action selection and motor control. We constructed a neural network model that proposes a specific neurobiological mechanism for stop signal reaction time performance, using the known dynamics and interactions of the basal ganglia. There are six groups of nuclei in our model: the cortex, the striatal dopamine D1 receptor expressing neurons, the striatal dopamine D2 receptor expressing

* Corresponding author: Joshua A. Burk, The College of William & Mary Department of Psychology, Williamsburg, VA 23187. Email address: jabur2@wm.edu.

neurons, the subthalamic nucleus (STN), the globus pallidus external segment (GPe), and an output population comprised of both the substantia nigra pars reticulata (SNr) and globus pallidus internal segment (GPi). We used a stochastic version of a Wilson-Cowan-type system of nonlinear differential equations to depict the spiking and synaptic activity of these neural populations. The firing rate of three different channels within the SNr/GPi neuron population representing three different actions can be monitored to determine if a particular action was selected in the simulation. Our model was able to reproduce general phenomena observed in the stop signal reaction time task in previous experiments and behavioral data that we collected from a group of rats trained in a stop signal reaction time task. Collectively, these results suggest that a population-level model can be used to understand the contribution of the basal ganglia to action selection.

Keywords: Action selection, basal ganglia, stop signal reaction time, Wilson-Cowan model

Abbreviations

STN	subthalamic nucleus
GPe	globus pallidus external segment
GPi	globus pallidus internal segment
SNr	substantia nigra reticulum
D1	striatal dopamine D1 receptor expressing neurons
D2	striatal dopamine D2 receptor expressing neurons
GCx	cortical input into the "Go" pathway
SCx	cortical input into the "Stop" pathway

1. Introduction

A failure of response inhibition is associated with several psychological disorders, including attention deficit hyperactivity disorder (ADHD; Nichols and Waschbusch, 2004). The severity of the response inhibition impairment can predict the response of individuals with ADHD to pharmacological interventions (van der Oord et al., 2012). The stop signal reaction time (SSRT) task has been commonly used to study response inhibition (Alderson et al., 2007; Band and van Boxtel, 1999). In SSRT tasks, the participant or subject is required to make a relatively simple, well-trained response. However, on a specific proportion of trials, a stop signal is presented. When this stop signal is presented, the well-trained response should be withheld. This task has been used with humans and with rats and is thought to have high translational potential (Eagle et al., 2008; Winstanley et al., 2006).

Specific basal ganglia structures are known to contribute to SSRT performance. For example, lesions of the dorsomedial striatum impair the stopping process, while administration of dopamine D1 and D2 ligands into the dorsomedial striatum differentially impact SSRT task performance (Eagle et al., 2011). Moreover, lesions of the nucleus accumbens have little effect on the SSRT task (Eagle and Robbins, 2003a,b), whereas lesions of the subthalamic nucleus disrupt SSRT task performance by preventing correct activation of the stopping process (Eagle et al., 2008). These findings highlight that multiple regions within the basal ganglia contribute to inhibition as measured by the SSRT task. Thus, the available data offer the opportunity to specify a model with particular basal ganglia structures that are critical to this task.

Computational models can be useful for understanding how the dynamics of multiple neural structures change while engaged in a task. To our knowledge, no available studies have employed single unit recording from the basal ganglia during SSRT task performance. The development of computational models of the activity of the neural structures underlying SSRT task performance may be useful for supporting hypothesis-driven experiments that employ measures of neuronal firing rates during SSRT task performance. An additional goal for the present project is to further refine available neural models of response inhibition. Previous rate-based and conductance-based spiking neuron models including multiple neuron populations have been used to predict and explain the process of action selection in the basal ganglia (Humphries et al., 2006, Gurney et al., 2001a, b, Girard et al., 2008). It remains unclear, however, whether a Wilson-Cowan population activity neural model is sufficient to predict SSRT task performance. In brief, this type of model is a set of differential equations that describes the aggregate activity of many neurons within a population (Destexhe and Sejnowski, 2009). In our case, the activity is given by a mean firing rate, which is determined in part through a nonlinear transformation of the inputs to a neural population (see Materials and Methods). Not only is this model one of the simpler methods to describe the mean activity of a large number of neurons, but it also allows for a more direct connection between the output of the model with the output of

SSRT experiments under the assumption that mean firing rates of the considered populations drive action selection.

We examined whether this population-level model is sufficient to describe the contribution of the basal ganglia during performance of the SSRT. We validated the computational model in several ways. We investigated whether our Wilson-Cowan-type model could reproduce the effects of a previously published leaky integrate-and-fire model (Humphries et al., 2006), assessed whether our model could reproduce reported changes in SSRT performance following manipulation of task parameters or drug administration and tested whether the model could reproduce a distribution of response latencies from empirical data collected from rats in our laboratories.

2. Methods

2.1. Experimental Methods

2.1.1. Subjects
Subjects included nine male FBNF1 hybrid rats (Harlan Laboratories), weighing 151-175 g at the beginning of the experiment. Rats were housed in a temperature- and humidity-controlled vivarium. Rats had *ad libitum* access to food throughout the experiment. Subjects received water for accurate task performance and for 30-min immediately following each testing session in their home cage. Animals were tested 5-6 days per week. Animals received at least 1 hour of water access on days they were not tested. All procedures were approved by the College of William & Mary Animal Care and Use Committee and animals were treated consistently with the Guide of the Care and Use of Laboratory Animals.

2.1.2. Apparatus
Rats were trained in chambers enclosed within sound-attenuating boxes (Med Associates, Inc., Georgia, VT). Two retractable levers, with a dipper between the levers were located on one side of each chamber. There were photocells to detect head entries in the water port containing the dipper. A panel light was located above each lever. A houselight in the back of the chamber provided diffuse illumination throughout the testing session. The illuminance levels for these chambers have been previously reported (Burk, 2004).

2.1.3. Stop Signal Reaction Time Task

Animals were trained using procedures similar to those described by other laboratories (Eagle and Robbins, 2003a,b). For one session, rats received water access (dipper raised for 3 s to allow access to 0.01 ml tap water) whenever entering the water port. After receiving 100 rewards in a session, rats were shaped to press the left lever. On these trials, a nosepoke into the water port caused the left lever to extend. The illumination of the central panel light indicated when the nosepoke could occur. The dipper in the water port was raised for 3 sec following a left lever press. This training continued until rats received 100 rewards within one session. During the next stage of training, a trial began with a nosepoke into the water port, which led to extension of the left lever. After a press on the left lever, the right lever was extended and a press on the right lever within the limited hold (initially 3 s) caused the right lever to be retracted and the dipper to be raised for 3 sec. These sessions lasted for 40 min.

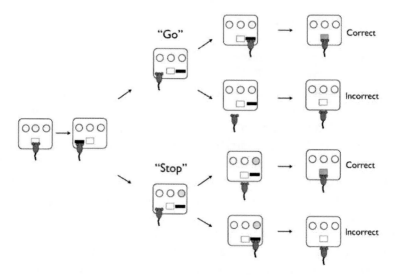

Figure 1. Diagrammatic representation of stop signal reaction time test. An experimental trial is initiated by a nose poke into the water port that triggers an extension of the left lever. A left lever push initiates an extension of the right lever. In 20% of the trials, the right lever extension is paired with a stop signal, i.e., illumination of the panel light. In a "Go" Trial, pushing the right lever is the correct response; in this case, a right lever push results in a reward from the water port. In a "Stop" Trial, refraining from pushing the right lever is the correct response; if this does not occur within a specified duration (i.e., a limited hold) the response is considered correct and rewarded.

During the next stage of training, the stop signal was introduced. A trial would begin with illumination of the central panel light, indicating that a nosepoke could initiate a trial. After a nosepoke, the left lever was extended. After a press on the left lever, the right lever was extended. A press on the right lever within 3 s was considered correct and water access was provided. On 20% of the trials, the panel light over the right lever was illuminated when the left lever was pressed. Illumination of the right panel light served as the stop signal. Initially, on stop signal trials, if rats withheld pressing the right lever for 1 s, water access was provided. The limited hold was slowly adjusted by 100-200 ms until it was the same for "Go" trials and "Stop" trials. For all rats, the final limited hold was 1.4 or 1.5 s. Animals were then tested for two sessions under these conditions in order to generate a sufficient number of trials to compare with results generated by our model. Figure 1 depicts an overview of performance in the final task.

2.2. Model Neural Network Architecture and Function

Figure 2 shows a diagram of the Wilson-Cowan-type network model that is the focus of this paper. The basal ganglia nuclei represented by the model include the striatal dopamine D1 receptor expressing neurons (D1), the striatal dopamine D2 receptor expressing neurons (D2), the subthalamic nucleus (STN), the external segment of the globus pallidus (GPe), the substantia nigra pars reticulata (SNr), and the globus pallidus internal segment (GPi, the latter two populations make up a single output population). Each of these nuclei is divided into three neural sub-populations or "channels" that are associated with alternative behaviors: left lever press (channel 1, blue), right lever press (channel 2, green), and all other actions (channel 3, red). Each channel, although segregated from each other, is identical in every aspect with the exception of the action that they encode. This framework is designed to correspond to the known physiology of the microcircuits within the basal ganglia (Bolam et al., 2000; Redgrave et al., 1999; Smith et al., 1998).

The network architecture within the Wilson-Cowan-type population-activity model of the basal ganglia presented here, i.e., the neural populations represented and synaptic connectivity, follows prior work (Humphries et al., 2006; Gurney, 2009; Gurney et al., 2001b). As shown in Figure 2, cortical drive influences the basal ganglia through excitatory input to the STN and the striatum (D1- and D2-receptor expression populations). The former connection is termed the "hyperdirect" pathway (Utter et al., 2008). The level of cortical input into a channel represents the salience of that action (Redgrave et al., 1999). For the purpose of clarity in our model, we have separated cortical input into two types: cortical input into the Go pathway, and cortical input into the Stop pathway (see below for definitions; Lei et al., 2004). We have termed the former "Go" cortex (GCx) and the latter "Stop" cortex (SCx). Although previous models have driven the activity of the two pathways not through separate cortical populations but through tonic dopamine levels (Humphries et al., 2006; Gurney, 2009; Gurney et al., 2001b), where increasing background dopamine levels activates the striatum D1 population but suppresses the striatum D2 population, recent literature suggests that the cortex preferentially projects to the Go or Stop pathway (Lei et al., 2004). It may be the case that both mechanisms are at work, but we did not consider dopaminergic volume as a parameter in our population-activity model. Although cortical input separately influences all three channels, for clarity only the input associated with channel 2 is shown in the diagram (right lever press, green). The D1 receptor expressing striatal population has an inhibitory and channel-specific projection to the SNr/GPi population. Conversely, the projection from the STN to the SNr/GPi is both excitatory and "diffuse," that is, channel 2 STN neurons project to channel 2 SNr/GPi neurons and, in addition, the SNr/GPi neurons associated with channels 1 and 3. As a consequence of this synaptic architecture, the cortical drive associated with channel 2 propagates through D1 and STN providing "off-center on-surround" input to the SNr/GPi. Suppression of channel 2 activity and enhancement of channels 1 and 3 increases the likelihood of selection of action 2 (see below). We will refer to this well-known mechanism of action selection as the "Go pathway". Note that the network architecture is symmetric with respect to the three channels and, consequently, the model includes a parallel pathway for selection of actions 1 and 3 (left lever press and other actions, respectively; not shown).

The D2 receptor expressing striatum population (D2), similar to D1, has an inhibitory and channel-specific projection to the GPe population. In turn, the GPe sends direct inhibitory output to the SNr/GPi, as well as direct inhibitory output to the STN. In return, the STN sends diffuse excitatory projections to the GPe. When cortical input into D2 is increased, the primary effect is inhibition of the GPe, which then relieves inhibition on the SNr/GPi.

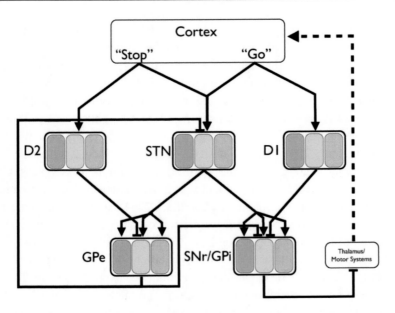

Figure 2. Representation of basal ganglia neural network. Shown are five basal ganglia populations and the corresponding cortical drive implemented in the model. The cortical input is divided into two subpopulations: one controlling action selection, termed the "Go cortex" (GCx), and another controlling action suppression, termed the "Stop cortex" (SCx). Each basal ganglia population is divided into three subpopulations, where each subpopulation is called a "channel." Each channel is depicted by a color within each population (blue is channel 1, green is channel 2, red is channel 3). Each channel corresponds to a unique action. For clarity, we have only shown the connectivity between channel 2 (green). The pointed arrow represents excitation, while the bar represents inhibition. The GCx sends excitatory projections to the striatum possessing the D1 dopamine receptors (D1), which then sends inhibitory projections to substantia nigra pars reticulata (SNr) and globus pallidus internal segment (GPi), which together function as the output population. The GABAergic SNr/GPi sends inhibitory projections to the brainstem and thalamus; the latter sends excitatory projections back to the cortex. Thus, inhibition of the SNr/GPi relieves inhibition on the thalamus and brainstem, which aids action selection. Accordingly, the D1 to SNr/GPi pathway is termed the "Go pathway". Alternatively, the "Stop cortex" sends excitatory projections to the striatum possessing the D2 dopamine receptors (D2). These neurons in turn send inhibitory projections to the GPe, which send inhibitory GABAergic projections to the STN and SNr/GPi populations. Thus, increased activity of the striatum D2 will decrease activity in the GPe, which in turn will remove inhibition from the output neurons, and suppress the activity of the brainstem and thalamocortical neurons. Accordingly, this pathway is termed the "Stop pathway." In addition, the Go and Stop cortex both send excitatory glutamatergic projections to the STN, which sends diffuse excitatory glutamatergic input to the GPe and SNr/GPi populations.

This allows the output population activity to remain above threshold, and thus the D2-GPe-SNr/GPi pathway is termed the "Stop pathway". The Stop and Go pathways converge at the level of the SNr/GPi, which functions as the output population in the network. In addition, the STN plays an important role in the action selection process. Generally, the STN is thought to be essential for the prevention of premature action selection (Frank, 2006), and the hyperdirect pathway is involved the suppression of action selection (Graybiel, 2005).

The SNr/GPi sends channel-specific inhibitory projections to the thalamus, which sends excitatory projections to the cortex. Thus, suppression of the SNr/GPi disinhibits the thalamus, which in turn excites various areas of the cortex to promote an action. This completes the cortico-basal ganglia-thalamic circuit, which has conventionally been described as a parallel and segregated pathway (Haber and Calzavara, 2009; Mink, 1996; Parent and Hazrati, 1995). In our population-activity model, we follow previous literature (Humphries et al., 2006) in monitoring the SNr/GPi activity as the output population and the indicator of action selection.

Action selection for a specific action begins when the corresponding SNr/GPi channel activity goes sufficiently beneath a threshold firing rate, denoted θ and chosen to be 5 Hz (Humphries et al., 2006). The SNr/GPi channel activity below this threshold is integrated and an action is selected when this accumulated suppression reaches a prescribed value, denoted $\bar{\theta}$. This is a modification of the approach taken by Humphries et al., 2006, but our approach allows for signal integration and latencies that are similar to those of empirical findings (Eagle et al., 2011; Eagle and Robbins, 2003). Selection of an action turns off the cortical input to that channel and restarts the calculation of the accumulated suppression. Model responses occur in distinct phases associated with the different stages of the simulated SSRT task ("left lever press," "right lever press," etc.). During each phase, a particular configuration of cortical drive propagates in a feed-forward manner throughout the represented basal ganglia populations. However, model responses include feedback as well as feed-forward dynamics, because the simulated SSRT task progresses to each subsequent phase based on selected actions (i.e., suppression of SNr/GPi output) that change the configuration of the cortical drive in a "closed loop" fashion (dashed line).

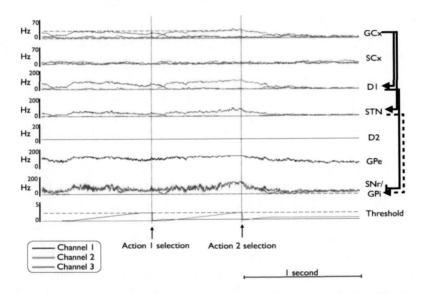

Figure 3. Basal ganglia population firing rate over time during a "Go" trial. This figure shows the solutions to our stochastic Wilson-Cowan model that describes the basal ganglia population activity during a "Go" trial (one without presentation of a stop signal). The blue trajectory corresponds to activity in channel 1 (left lever press) of each population, the green trajectory corresponds to activity in channel 2 (right lever press), and the red trajectory corresponds to activity in channel 3 (all other actions). The trial begins with an increase of the Go cortical input of channel 1. The increased activity flows through the network and the activity of the output neurons (SNr/GPi) is monitored. The relevant connections between the neural populations are shown on the left; the solid line indicates direct projections while the dashed line indicates diffuse projections. The integrated area between the firing rate threshold (θ, 5 Hz) and the SNr/GPi channel activity is calculated and this dimensionless quantity is plotted in the bottom plot. Once the value of this integral crosses the selection threshold $\bar{\theta}$, the action for channel 1 is selected, and the cortical input to channel 1 turns off while the Go cortical input to channel 2 turns on. The dotted blue and green lines on the top plot represent the mean cortical input, while the vertical dotted black lines show the time of action selection for channels 1 and 2.

For example, changes in neural activity leading to the left lever press at the beginning of a "Go" trial (see Figure 3) are evoked in the model by an increase in GCx to channel 1 (blue) of both the D1 and the STN. Increased activity in these sub-populations ultimately leads to suppression of the activity of channel 1 output neurons in the SNr/GPi. Although the resulting disinhibition of thalamocortical neurons is not explicitly modeled, the selection of the left lever press action changes the cortical drive associated with the new experimental context. This evokes an increase in Go cortical drive (GCx) to channel 2 (green), and again, this increased activity ultimately leads to suppression of channel 2 output neurons in the SNr/GPi. Selection of the "right lever press" action ends the "Go" trial. In the case of the "Stop" trial, the increase in Go cortical drive into channel 2 is paired with an increase in SCx into channel 2. This activates the Stop pathway, and the Go and Stop pathways compete at the level of the channel 2 output neurons. In a successful stop signal trial, the Stop pathway activation is strong enough to prevent selection of the left lever press action.

2.3. Computational Model

The computational model is a Wilson-Cowan-type system of nonlinear differential equations for the activity of multiple populations of interacting neurons (Wilson and Cowan, 1972; for review see Destexhe and Sejnowski, 2009). Under the assumption that the membrane time constant is fast compared to the synaptic time course, the Wilson-Cowan equations take the form (Pinto et al., 1996; Ermentrout, 1998)

$$\tau \frac{da_i}{dt} + a_i = f_i\left(h_i + \sum_j w_{ij} a_j\right)$$

where the dependent variable a_i is the activity or "synaptic drive" associated with neural population i, τ is the synaptic decay time constant (assumed to be the same for all populations), w_{ij} represents the connectivity of the network of neural populations, that is, w_{ij} represents the strength of the connection from population j to i , and h_i represents external drive (cortical input, see below). The right hand side of this differential equation is the firing rate of neural population i, here given by the sigmoidal function

$$f_i(s_i) = \frac{f_i^{max}}{1 + \exp\left(-\dfrac{s_i - \sigma_i^0}{\sigma_i^1}\right)}$$

where $s_i = h_i + \sum_j w_{ij} a_j$ is the presynaptic input to population i. The maximum firing rate and location and scale parameters may vary according to neural population (see Table 1) because the striatum (f_{D1}^{max} and f_{D2}^{max}) are known to have a lower firing rate than the other neural populations (f_{STN}^{max}, f_{GPe}^{max} and $f_{SNr/GPi}^{max}$) (Mink, 1996).

Table 1. Model parameters

Parameter	Constraints	Value	Units	Reference
$W_{STN,SNr/GPi}$	> 0, $< \|D1_{SNr/GPi}\|$	14	-	Humphries et al., 2006; Mink, 1996
$W_{D1,SNr/GPi}$	< 0	−22	-	Ibid
$W_{D2,GP}$	< 0	−22	-	Ibid
$W_{GPe,STN}$	< 0	−2	-	Ibid
$W_{STN,GPe}$	$> 0, \approx$ STN, SNr/GPi	12	-	Ibid
$W_{GPe,SNr/GPi}$	< 0	−2	-	Ibid
$W_{Cx,D1}$	> 0	0.1	-	-
$W_{Cx,D2}$	> 0	0.1	-	-
σ_i^1	-	1	Hz	-
σ_{D1}^0	$D1_{spon} = 5$ Hz	2.56	Hz	Mink, 1996
σ_{STN}^0	$STN_{spon} = 20\,Hz$	2.20	Hz	Bevan et al., 1999
$\sigma_{SNr/GPi}^0$	$SNr/GPi_{spon} = 30\,Hz$	1.73	Hz	Humphries et al., 2006
σ_{D2}^0	$D2_{spon} = 5\,Hz$	2.56	Hz	Mink, 1996
σ_{GPe}^0	$GPe_{spon} = 30\,Hz$	1.73	Hz	Humphries et al., 2006
τ	$0 < \tau < 1$	0.01	s	-
τ_{STN}	$< \tau$	0.001	s	-
τ_h	> 0	0.2	s	-
γ_h	> 0	100	s^{-3}	-
θ	> 0	5	Hz	Humphries et al., 2006
$\bar{\theta}$	> 0	3	-	-
$f_{STN}^{max}, f_{GPe}^{max}, f_{SNr/GPi}^{max}$	$0 < x < 1000$	200	Hz	-
$f_{D1}^{max}, f_{D2}^{max}$	$0 < x < 100$	70	Hz	Mink, 1996

The cortical input contains a stochastic element that is meant to represent the noise in the mean population activity that arises from containing a finite number of neurons. The differential equation representing the cortical input takes the following form:

$$\frac{dh_i}{dt} = \frac{-(h_i - \overline{h_i})}{\tau_h} + \xi_i(t)$$

where τ_h is the decay time constant (assumed to be the same for both GCx and SCx), and $\overline{h_i}$ is the mean cortical input, represented as the dotted lines in the top two panels of Figures 3 and 4. The time-dependent variable $\xi_i(t)$ represents Gaussian white noise terms with $\langle \xi_i(t) \rangle = 0$, and a two-time covariance given by $\langle \xi_i(t)\xi_j(t') \rangle = \gamma_{ij}\delta(t - t')$, where $\gamma_{ij} = 0$ for $i \neq j$, and δ is the dirac-delta function.

Table 1 lists the parameters used and their respective chosen values. The spontaneous and maximum firing rates of the populations, along with the general values of the cortical input, were found in the literature (Bevan and Wilson, 1999; Mink, 1996). The value of σ_0 is constrained by the spontaneous firing rate of each population (Table 1). Parameter regimes for synaptic weights are based on the known physiology of the population (Bevan and Wilson, 1999; Humphries and Gurney, 2002; Humphries et al., 2006; Mink, 1996). Specific values for these synaptic weights, time constants, the parameters for the stochastic process, and the selection threshold were found through parameter studies.

3. Results

3.1. Population Firing Rates during "Go" and "Stop" Trials

We analyzed the firing rates of each population on "Go" trials, i.e. trials without presentation of a stop signal. The top two panels of Figure 3 show the two varieties of cortical input; in "Go" trials, only the selection cortex (top panel) is pertinent. The simulation shows the activity for three channels: channel 1 (blue), channel 2 (green), and channel 3 (red), where each channel corresponds to a specific action. As the simulation begins, selection cortical input into channel 1 "turns on," i.e. steps from 0 to 40, which corresponds to cortical input for the left lever press action. The mean cortical input for each channel is shown as the dotted line in the top panel. This input increases the firing rate of the channel 1 striatum D1 neurons (in the selection pathway) and the channel 1 STN neurons. These two populations (D1 and STN) converge on the SNr/GPi channel 1 subpopulation and thus compete at the level of the output neurons. The diffuse excitatory projections of the STN also serve to highlight the channel under direct inhibition from D1, as the neighboring channels are excited in an off-center, on-surround manner. Sufficient inhibition of an output subpopulation leads to action selection for the action corresponding to that subpopulation. In our model, selection of the left lever press action is determined by the continuous integration of the SNr/GPi channel 1 firing rate under a given threshold firing rate, taken to be 5 Hz (Humphries et al., 2006). The bottom panel of Figure 3 shows the accumulating magnitude of suppression of firing rate below threshold firing rate for both channel 1 (blue) and channel 2 (green); selection occurs when the integrated suppression crosses the selection threshold (see Materials and Methods). When a specific action is selected, the integration for that channel is reset to 0 in preparation for the next phase of the task.

Once the left lever press action is selected, cortical input for that action "turns off," i.e. steps from 40 to 0, as the salience for that particular action sharply decreases. In turn, the next action - the right lever press - becomes the most salient action, and cortical activation turns on for channel 2 (right lever press). Again, selection of that action is determined by the continuous integration of the channel 2 firing rate under a threshold firing rate. Figure 3 shows selection of the left lever press action followed by selection of the right lever press action.

We also examined neural network dynamics when a stop signal is presented immediately after the left lever press (zero delay). The results are shown in Figure 4. The first part of the simulation is similar to trials with no stop signal: cortical activation for channel 1 (the left lever press pathway) turns on, which increases the activity in the channel 1 striatum D1 neurons and inhibits the channel 1 SNr/GPi neurons. Again, the channel 1 SNr/GPi population must be sufficiently inhibited in order for that action to be selected. Once that action is selected, cortical activation for a right lever press turns on as the cortical activation for the left lever press turns off. At the same time, the stop signal is presented, thus activating the Stop pathway. The Stop pathway increases activity in the channel 2 Striatum D2 subpopulation, which then inhibits the channel 2 GPe neurons. In turn, the channel 2 GPe subpopulation inhibits the corresponding subpopulation of the SNr/GPi. Thus, inhibition of the channel 2 GPe population disinhibits the channel 2 SNr/GPi population, and ultimately prevents action selection by prohibiting the output subpopulation from being sufficiently inhibited. Note that the channel 2 (green) line on the bottom panel does not cross the selection threshold during the trial.

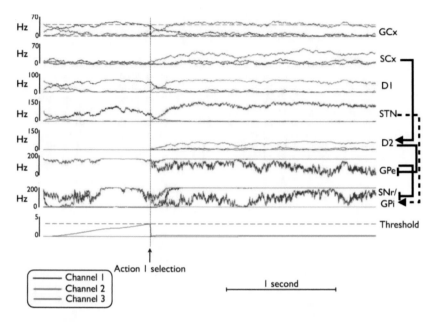

Figure 4. Basal ganglia population firing rate over time during a "Stop" trial. This figure shows the solutions to the stochastic Wilson-Cowan model that describes the basal ganglia population activity during a "Stop" trial (one with the presentation of a stop signal). At the start of the trial, Go cortical input increases in channel 1, and the increased activity goes through the network, ultimately suppressing the SNr/GPi channel 1 population. Once this population is sufficiently suppressed, that is, when the area between the channel 1 activity and the threshold firing rate θ crosses a selection threshold $\overline{\theta}$, action 1 is selected. After this event, i.e. a left lever press, the cortical input for channel 2 (a right lever press) turns on. The cortical input for the Stop pathway in channel 2 then turns on. The Go pathway and the Stop pathway compete at the level of the SNr/GPi output neurons. The area between the threshold and SNr/GPi channel 2 activity must pass a threshold in order for channel 2 to be selected. This threshold is not crossed in this figure, which means that the response was successfully withheld for the duration of the trial.

3.2. Comparison of Results from the Present Population-Based Model and a Conductance-Based Model

One of the major goals of this project is to assess whether a population-based neural model can yield similar results to an integrate-and-fire model with regard to basal ganglia processing underlying SSRT task performance. We compared our model with the spiking model described in Humphries et al. (2006) in several respects.

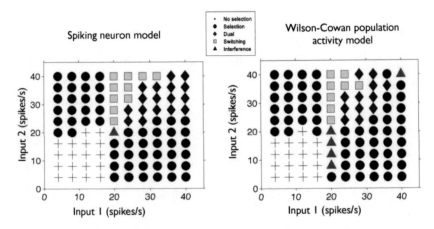

Figure 5. Action selection capabilities of the model. The left panel of this figure is an adaptation of integrate-and-fire neural network simulation results presented in Figure 4A of Humphries et al. (2006). Shown to the right are corresponding results of the stochastic Wilson-Cowan-type population activity model that is the focus of this paper. In both cases, each trial simulation is five seconds, and there are two cortical inputs: input 1 and input 2. Input 1 turns on 1 second into the trial, and input 2 turns on 2.5 seconds into the trial. Only the Go pathway is directly involved in these trials; input 1 activates channel 1, and input 2 activates channel 2. Once an input turns on, it is on for the duration of the trial. Based upon the SNr/GPi channel activity in the time series, the trial will fall into a selection category. There are five different selection categories: No Selection (black plus), Single Selection (blue circle), Dual Selection (green diamond), Switching (yellow square), and Interference (red diamond). The figure shows the selection categories for each level of input ranging from 10-40.

Humphries et al. (2006) reported the findings from a parameter study that characterized the type of selection given different cortical input levels through two different channels. The first cortical input begins when t = 1 and lasts until t = 5 seconds, while the second cortical input begins when t = 2.5 and lasts until t = 5 seconds. Phase 1 is from t = 1 to t = 2.5, while phase 2 is from t = 2.5 to t = 5 seconds. There were four types of action selection that were characterized: single selection, dual selection, no selection, and switching selection. Any other selection category was labeled as interference. Action selection is again characterized as above; an action is selected when the SNr/GPi firing rate of a specific channel is sufficiently beneath a threshold, that is, the area between the channel firing rate and the threshold firing rate crosses a selection threshold. Single selection occurs when action 1 is selected in phase 1 and phase 2, or action 2 is selected in phase 2. Dual selection occurs when action 1 is selected in phase 1 and phase 2, and action 2 is selected in phase 2. Switching selection occurs when action 1 is selected in phase 1 and deselected in phase 2, and action 2 is selected in phase 2. No selection occurs when neither action 1 nor action 2 are selected in phase 1 or phase 2. Interference includes all other possibilities. For example, interference will occur if only action 1 is selected only during phase 2. As can be observed in Figure 5, results from our model are qualitatively similar to those from Humphries et al. (2006).

3.3. Comparison of The Model Output with Empirical Measures of SSRT Task Performance

One effect that has been previously reported in the SSRT task is that accuracy decreases as the time between the initiated response (left lever press in experiments with rats) and onset of the stop signal increases (Eagle et al., 2003b). We investigated how well the population-based model predicts changes in accuracy as the onset of the stop signal is varied (Figure 6). In our model simulation, we used a cortical inputs GCx = 40 spikes/s and SCx = 30 spikes/s, and varied the onset of the stop signal time by varying onset of the activation of the Stop pathway. Our model simulation indicates that the probability of accurately inhibiting a response decreases approximately linearly as the stop signal delay is increased. These results are similar to those in the literature (e.g., Eagle and Robbins, 2003b).

The effects of dopamine-1 receptor (D1R) and dopamine-2 receptor (D2R) antagonists have also been tested in the SSRT task (Eagle et al., 2011). D1R blockade decreases SSRT whereas D2R blockade increases SSRT (Eagle et al., 2011). We simulated the effects of D1R blockade by decreasing the strength of the inputs to the D1-expressing striatum population; in the present population-activity model this corresponds to decreasing our default GCx cortical input value of 40 to 36, 32, 28 and 24 (90%, 80%, 70%, and 60% of the original value respectively). The results in SSRT task performance are shown in the top panel of Figure 7. We observed that SSRT systematically decreased as the cortical input was decreased, similar to the results of Eagle et al. (2011) following D1R antagonist administration. We then examined the effect of decreasing the input (SCx) to D2Rs by 10%, 20%, 30% and 40% to model increasing levels of D2R antagonist (Figure 7, bottom panel). Consistent with effects of D2R blockade by Eagle et al. (2011), we observed increases in SSRT when D2R input was decreased.

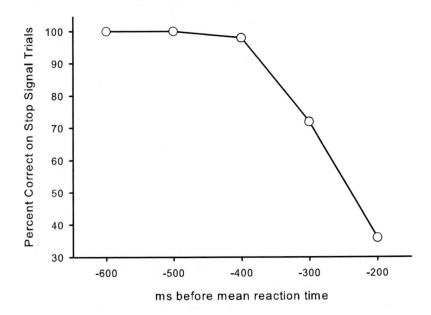

Figure 6. Increasing the stop signal delay. We tested the effects of increasing the stop signal delay on accuracy in the "Stop" trials in the model. The x-axis depicts the stop signal delay and the y-axis depicts accuracy on stop signal trials. As observed in previous SSRT task experiments (e.g. Eagle et al., 2003a), increasing the stop signal delay decreases the probability of correctly withholding a response on a "Stop" trial.

As a further test of our model, we collected data from rats in our laboratory regarding response latencies on "Go" trials. Specifically, we collected latencies from the left lever press to the right lever press on "Go" trials. Our goal was to examine whether the distribution of latencies was similar in our model as in the empirical data. Figure 8 shows the empirically measured response latencies (left) and the model response latencies (right). Each latency data point is scaled by the individual maximum allowed latency of each rat in order to account for differences between the subjects. The red curves fitting both data sets are gamma probability density functions with the same mean and variance as the data. Thus, the distribution of response latencies from our stochastic model was similar to the distribution from the experimental data.

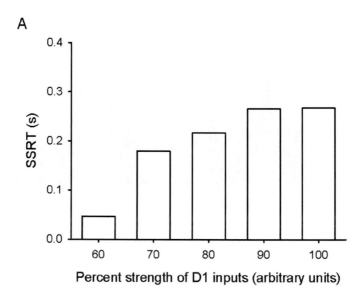

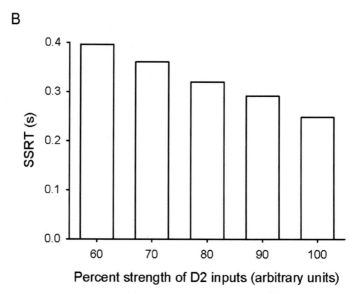

Figure 7. Simulated SSRT task effect of D1R blockade and D2R blockade. We examined, in the model, the effect of weakening inputs onto D1R and D2R expressing neurons on the SSRT. Similar to empirical findings, the SSRT decreases as D1R inputs are decreased (top panel), while SSRT increases as D2R inputs are decreased (bottom panel).

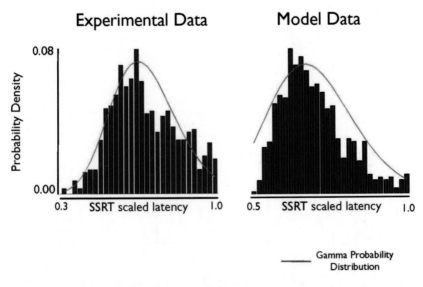

Figure 8. Probability Distribution of Response latency on "Go" trials. We tested whether the distribution of response latencies on "Go" trials was similar between the model and empirical data that we collected. Both the experimental data and the simulated data contain a total of 695 total trials. The bars represent the SSRT task latencies from nine rats. The simulated latencies are scaled by the individual maximum allowed latency of each rat in order to account for differences between the subjects. The red curves show Gamma distributions with the same mean and variance as experimental data. The parameters used for the experimental data gamma distribution are used in the gamma distribution for the simulated data. Please note that the x-axis for the experimental data (left panel) ranges from 0.3 to 1.0, while the x-axis for the Model Data (right panel) ranges from 0.5 to 1.0.

4. Discussion

The present project examined whether a Wilson-Cowan-type population activity model of cortico-basal ganglia processing could be successful in predicting performance in a stop signal reaction time task. Although rate-based and spiking neural models have been developed to investigate action selection in the basal ganglia, ours is the first to consider the stop signal reaction time task. Furthermore, in contrast with the previously published models of action selection in the basal ganglia done by Humphries et al., 2006, Gurney et al., 2001a, Gurney et al., 2001b, and Girard et al., 2008, we included two types of stochastic cortical input that differentially innervate the striatum D1 and striatum D2. Additionally, we included signal integration in the method of action selection. First, we assessed whether the output regarding action selection was similar between our model and a previously published model that used an integrate-and-fire modeling approach (Humphries et al., 2006). We found that the models led to very similar output patterns when the parameters for input 1 and input 2 were systematically varied (Figure 5). We then examined whether our model could reproduce a basic phenomenon in stop signal reaction time task performance, namely that accuracy declines as the time between the initiation of the prepotent response and the stop signal is increased (Figure 6). Thus, the results from our model were consistent with those from published empirical work (Eagle and Robbins, 2003b). Moreover, the effects of D1R and D2R blockade on SSRT in our model were very similar to those reported in the literature (Figure 7) (Eagle et al., 2011). Finally, we examined whether our stochastic model could capture the qualitative aspects of the response latency probability distribution present in a group of rats trained in the stop signal reaction time task. Our model did yield a distribution of response latencies that was qualitatively similar to a distribution of response latencies collected from rats in our laboratory (Figure 8). Thus, our model provides a useful representation of the population-level dynamics that contribute to action selection.

The present model has several important limitations. First, this model does not differentiate between the pattern of spiking activity, nor between dopaminergic volume and phasic transmission (Frank, 2005). When this model is unable to reproduce observed phenomena, it may indicate a critical role for spiking activity or patterns of transmission (Humphries and Gurney, 2001). Moreover, the inability to manipulate these factors in the present model limits assessments of how changes in spiking activity and transmission mode contribute to observed phenomena. Second, the present manuscript primarily relates the model to observed patterns of behavior in rats. Rats were selected because their performance in this task appears to be comparable to humans and data were available regarding infusions of D1R and D2R antagonists into the dorsomedial striatum in rats. Nonetheless, the extent to which this model reflects underlying neural mechanisms in humans requires further study. Third, the model relies upon the important assumption that there are parallel and segregated loops within the basal ganglia architecture, that is, there is little overlap between the distinct channels, and the Stop and Go pathways are independent of each other. However, recent literature suggests that there is significant integration of processing among various channels, especially between channels that are spatially close within the basal ganglia (Haber and Calzavara, 2009). In addition, there may be cross-talk between the Go and

Stop pathways, namely due to axon collaterals that project to both the GPe and the output neurons (Frank, 2006; Redgrave et al., 2010; Wu et al., 2000). Although the assumption of parallel and segregated microcircuits within the basal ganglia is generally supported by the literature, this assumption does not entirely reflect the underlying neuroanatomy.

There are several ways in which the present model could be expanded. The thalamus was not directly included in the model, although it is part of the cortico-basal ganglia-thalamo-cortical loops that underlie action selection. Previous models also suggest that thalamo-cortical projections enhance action switching properties and further organize basal ganglia output (Humphries and Gurney, 2002). In addition, several regions within the thalamus provide dense topographically organized innervation of the striatum (Berendse and Groenewegen, 1990; Groenewegen et al., 1999a,b; Smith et al., 2004; Vertes, 2006). These thalamostriatal projections might contribute to communication between the parallel pathways through the basal ganglia (Haber and Calzavara, 2009; Mengual et al., 1999). Thus, this population-level model could be expanded by evaluating the impact of thalamic inputs to the striatum. This approach would be valuable for making predictions about the contribution of the thalamus to SSRT performance. Moreover, these thalamostriatal inputs preferentially project onto striatal cholinergic interneurons (Lapper and Bolam, 1992), which may have a significant role in mediating the Go and Stop pathways (Ding et al., 2010). Thus, the model may also be expanded by including a different population that represents striatal cholinergic interneurons. In summary, our results suggest that population-level dynamics represent a critical level of analysis for action selection and that this approach may be fruitful for understanding how multiple brain regions interact to contribute to SSRT task performance.

Acknowledgments

This work was supported in part by National Science Foundation (NSF) Grant 1121606 (GDS), a Faculty Interdisciplinary Research Grant through The College of William and Mary (GDS and JAB), an ALSAM scholarship through the College of William and Mary (KH), and a Howard Hughes Medical Institute grant through the Undergraduate Biological Sciences Education Program to The College of William and Mary (KH).

References

Alderson, RM; Rapport, MD; Kofler, MJ. Attention-deficit/hyperactivity disorder and behavioral inhibition: a meta-analytic review of the stop-signal paradigm. *J. Abnorm. Child Psychol*, 2007, 35, 745-758.

Band, GP; van Boxtel, GJ. Inhibitory motor control in stop paradigms: review and reinterpretation of neural mechanisms. *Acta Psychol. (Amst.)*, 2007, 101, 179-211.

Berendse, HW; Groenewegen, HJ. Organization of the thalamostriatal projections in the rat, with special emphasis on the ventral striatum. *J. Comp. Neurol.*, 1990, 299, 187-228.

Bevan, MD; Wilson, CJ. Mechanisms underlying spontaneous oscillation and rhythmic firing in rat subthalamic neurons. *J. Neurosci.*, 1999, 19, 7617-7628.

Bolam, JP; Hanley, JJ; Booth, PAC; Bevan, MD. Synaptic organization of the basal ganglia. *J. Anat.*, 2000, 196, 527-542.

Burk, JA. Introduction of a retention interval in a sustained attention task in rats: effects of presenting a visual distracter and increasing the inter-trial interval. *Behav. Processes*, 2004, 67, 521-531.

Destexhe, A; Sejnowski, TJ. The Wilson-Cowan model, 36 years later. *Biol. Cybern.*, 2009, 101, 1–2.

Ding, JB; Guzman, JN; Peterson, JD; Godberg, JA; Surmeier, DJ. Thalamic gating of corticostriatal signaling by cholinergic interneurons. *Neuron*, 2010, 67, 294-307.

Eagle, D; Baunez, C; Hutcheson, D; Lehmann, O; Shah, A; Robbins, T. Stop-signal reaction-time task performance: role of prefrontal cortex and subthalamic nucleus. *Cereb. Cortex*, 2008, 18, 178-188.

Eagle, DM; Robbins, TW. Inhibitory control in rats performing a stop-signal reaction-time task: effects of lesions of the medial striatum and d-amphetamine. *Behav. Neurosci.*, 2003a, 117, 1302-1317.

Eagle, DM; Robbins, TW. Lesions of the medial prefrontal cortex or nucleus accumbens core do not impair inhibitory control in rats performing a stop-signal reaction time task. Behav. *Brain Res.*, 2003b, 146, 131-144.

Eagle, DM; Wong, JCK; Allan, ME; Mar, AC; Theobald, DE; Robbins, TW. Contrasting roles for the dopamine D1 and D2 receptor subtypes in the dorsomedial striatum but not the nucleus accumbens core during behavioral inhibition in the stop-signal task in rats. *J. Neurosci.*, 2011, 31, 7349-7356.

Ermentrout, B. Neural networks as spatio-temporal pattern-forming systems. *Rep. Prog. Phys.*, 1998, 61, 353-430.

Frank, MJ. Dynamic dopamine modulation in the basal ganglia: a neurocomputational account of cognitive deficits in medicated and nonmedicated Parkinsonism. *J. Cogn. Neurosci.*, 2005, 17, 51-72.

Frank, MJ. Hold your horses: A dynamic computational role for the subthalamic nucleus in decision-making. *Neural Netw.*, 2006, 19, 1120-1136.

Graybiel, AM. The basal ganglia: learning new tricks and loving it. *Curr. Opin. Neurobiol.*, 2005, 15, 638-644.

Girard, B; Tabareau, N; Pham, QC; Berthoz, A; Slotine, JJ. Where neuroscience and dynamical system theory meet autonomous robotics: a contracting basal ganglia model for action selection. *Neural Netw.*, 2008, 21, 628-641.

Groenewegen HJ; Galis-de Graaf, Y; Smeets, WJ. Integration and segregation of limbic cortico-striatal loops at the thalamic level: an experimental tracing study in rats. *J. Chem. Neuroanat.*, 1999a, 16, 167-185.

Groenewegen, HJ; Wright, CI; Beijer, AV; Voorn, P. Convergence and segregation of ventral striatal inputs and outputs. *Ann. N. Y. Acad. Sci.*, 1999b, 877, 49-63.

Gurney, KN. Computational models in neuroscience: from membranes to robots. In: Mavritsake E, Heinke D editors. *Computational Modelling in Behavioural Neuroscience: Closing the Gap Between Neurophysiology and Behaviour* (Advances in Behavioural Brain Science). New York: Psychology Press: 2009, 107-136.

Gurney, K; Prescott, TJ; Redgrave, P. A computational model of action selection in the basal ganglia. I. A new functional anatomy. *Biol. Cybern.*, 2001a, 85, 401-410.

Gurney, K; Prescott, TJ; Redgrave, P. A computational model of action selection in the basal ganglia. II. Analysis and simulation of behavior. *Biol. Cybern.*, 2001b, 85, 411-423.

Haber, SN; Calzavara, R. The cortico-basal ganglia integrative network: the role of the thalamus. *Brain Res. Bull.*, 2009, 78, 69-74.

Humphries, MD; Gurney, KN. A pulsed neural network model of bursting in the basal ganglia. *Neural Netw.*, 2001, 14, 845-863.

Humphries, MD; Gurney, KN. The role of intra-thalamic and thalamocortical circuits in action selection. Network, 2002, 13, 131-156.

Humphries, MD; Stewart, RD; Gurney, KN. A physiologically plausible model of action selection and oscillatory activity in the basal ganglia. *J. Neurosci.*, 2006, 26, 12921-12942.

Lapper, SR; Bolam, JP. Input from the frontal cortex and the parafascicular nucleus to cholinergic interneurons in the dorsal striatum of the rat. *Neuroscience*, 1992, 51, 533-545.

Lei, W; Jiao, Y; Del Mar, N; Reiner, A. Evidence for differential cortical input to direct pathway versus indirect pathway striatal projection neuron in rats. *J. Neurosci.*, 2004, 24, 8289-8299.

Mengual, E; Heras, S; Erro, E; Lanciego, JL; Giménez-Amaya, JM. Thalamic interaction between the input and the output systems of the basal ganglia. *J. Chem. Neuroanat.*, 1999, 16, 187-200.

Mink, JW. The basal ganglia: focused selection and inhibition of competing motor programs. *Prog. Neurobiol.*, 1996, 50, 381-425.

Nichols, SL; Waschbusch, DA. A review of the validity of laboratory cognitive tasks used to assess symptoms of ADHD. *Child Psychiatry Hum. Dev.*, 2004, 34, 297-315.

Parent, A; Hazrati, LN. Functional anatomy of the basal ganglia. I. The cortico-basal ganglia-thalamo-cortical loop. *Brain Res. Rev.*, 1995, 20, 91-127.

Pinto, DJ; Brumbery, JC; Simons, DJ; Ermentrout, GB. A quantitative population model of whisker barrels: re-examining the Wilson-Cowan equations. *J. Comput. Neurosci.*, 1996, 3, 247-264.

Redgrave, P; Prescott, TJ; Gurney, K. The basal ganglia: a vertebrate solution to the selection problem? *Neuroscience*, 1999, 89, 1009-1023.

Redgrave, P; Rodriguez, M; Smith, Y; Rodriguez-Oroz, MC; Lehericy, S; Bergman, H; Agid, Y; DeLong, MR; Obeso, JA. Goal-directed and habitual control in the basal ganglia: implications for Parkinson's disease. *Nat. Rev. Neurosci.*, 2010, 11, 760-772.

Smith, Y; Bevan, MD; Shink, E; Bolam, JP. Microcircuitry of the direct and indirect pathways of the basal ganglia. *Neuroscience*, 1998, 86, 353-387.

Smith, Y; Raju, DV; Pare, J; Sidibe, M. The thalamostriatal system: a highly specific network of basal ganglia circuitry. *Trends Neurosci.*, 2004, 27, 520-527.

Utter, AA; Basso, MA. Basal ganglia: An overview of circuits and function. *Neurosci. Biobehav. Rev.*, 2008, 32, 333-342.

van der Oord, S; Geurts, HM; Prins, PJ; Emelkamp, PM; Oosterlaan, J. Prepotent response inhibition predicts treatment outcome in attention deficit/hyperactivity disorder. *Child Neuropsychol.*, 2002, 18, 50-61.

Vertes, RP. Interactions among the medial prefrontal cortex, hippocampus and midline thalamus in emotional and cognitive processing in the rat. *Neuroscience*, 2006, 142, 1-20.

Wilson, HR; Cowan, JD. Excitatory and inhibitory interactions in localized populations of model neurons. *Biophys. J.*, 1972, 12, 1-24.

Winstanley, CA; Eagle, DM; Robbins, TW. Behavioral models of impulsivity in relation to ADHD: translation between clinical and preclinical studies. *Clin. Psychol. Rev.*, 2006, 26, 379-395.

Wu, Y; Richard, S; Parent, A. The organization of the striatal output system: A single-cell juxtacellular labeling study in the rat. *Neurosci. Res.*, 2000, 38, 49-62.

In: Globus Pallidus   ISBN: 978-1-62948-367-2
Editors: C.R. Gordon, T.G. Abbadelli   © 2013 Nova Science Publishers, Inc.

Chapter 4

Neuropathology of the Basal Ganglia and its Role in the Parkinsonian Syndromes with Special Reference to the Globus Pallidus

*R. A. Armstrong**
Department of Vision Sciences, Aston
University, Birmingham, UK

Abstract

The globus pallidus, together with the striatum (caudate nucleus and putamen), substantia nigra, nucleus accumbens, and subthalamic nucleus constitute the basal ganglia, a group of nuclei which act as a single functional unit. The basal ganglia have extensive connections to the cerebral cortex and thalamus and exert control over a variety of functions including voluntary motor control, procedural learning, and motivation. The action of the globus pallidus is primarily inhibitory and balances the excitatory influence of other areas of the brain such as the cerebral cortex

* Corresponding author: R. A. Armstrong. Department of Vision Sciences, Aston University,
  Birmingham B4 7ET, UK. Tel: +44-121-204-4102, Fax: +44-121-204-4048, E-mail: R.A.
  Armstrong@aston.ac.uk.

and cerebellum. Neuropathological changes affecting the basal ganglia play a significant role in the clinical signs and symptoms observed in the 'parkinsonian syndromes' viz., Parkinson's disease (PD), progressive supranuclear palsy (PSP), dementia with Lewy bodies (DLB), multiple system atrophy (MSA), and corticobasal degeneration (CBD). There is increasing evidence that different regions of the basal ganglia are differentially affected in these disorders. Hence, in all parkinsonian disorders and especially PD, there is significant pathology affecting the substantia nigra and its dopamine projection to the striatum. However, in PSP and MSA, the globus pallidus is also frequently affected while in DLB and CBD, whereas the caudate nucleus and/or putamen are affected, the globus pallidus is often spared. This chapter reviews the functional pathways of the basal ganglia, with special reference to the globus pallidus, and the role that differential pathology in these regions may play in the movement disorders characteristic of the parkinsonian syndromes.

Keywords: Globus pallidus, Basal ganglia, Parkinsonian disorders, Substantia nigra, Striatum, Parkinson's disease (PD), Lewy bodies (LB)

Introduction

A number of disorders are included within the 'parkinsonian' syndromes, a group of disorders which includes Parkinson's disease (PD) (Armstrong, 2008), progressive supranuclear palsy (PSP) (Armstrong, 2011), dementia with Lewy bodies (DLB) (Armstrong et al., 1998; Armstrong, 2012), multiple system atrophy (MSA) (Armstrong et al., 2004), and corticobasal degeneration (CBD) (Armstrong et al., 2009) (Table 1). In many of these disorders, the patient exhibits a variety of movement problems most commonly akinesia, rigidity, tremor, gait problems, and myoclonus.

The globus pallidus, together with the striatum, substantia nigra, nucleus accumbens, and subthalamic nucleus constitute the basal ganglia, a group of nuclei which act as a single functional unit. The basal ganglia have extensive connections to the cerebral cortex, thalamus, and cerebellum and exert control over a variety of functions including voluntary motor control, procedural learning, and motivation. The specific action of the globus pallidus is inhibitory and it balances the excitatory influence of other areas of the brain such as the cerebral cortex and cerebellum. Neuropathological changes affecting the basal ganglia play a significant role in the clinical signs and symptoms observed in the parkinsonian syndromes.

Hence, it is possible that differential pathology in these regions could lead to differences in movement problems in the various parkinsonian syndromes.

This chapter describes: (1) the clinical and pathological features of the various parkinsonian syndromes, (2) the functional pathways of the basal ganglia and the specific role of the globus pallidus, and (3) differential pathology in the basal ganglia and its possible significance in determining the various movement problems of the parkinsonian syndromes.

Basal Ganglia

The globus pallidus is part of the basal ganglia, a large mass of gray matter located at the base of the forebrain, and which act together as a functional unit (Brodal, 1981). The basal ganglia are intimately connected to other areas of brain including the cerebral cortex, thalamus, and cerebellum. The major components of the basal ganglia are the striatum, comprising the caudate nucleus and putamen, globus pallidus, substantia nigra, nucleus accumbens, and subthalamic nucleus. The three-dimensional structure of the basal ganglia is shown in Figure 1. The caudate nucleus has a relatively large anterior portion, known as the head, and which is directly connected to the putamen. The rest of the caudate nucleus forms an arch of continuously diminishing size curving around the thalamus and lateral to it. The slender part of the tail proceeds in a rostral direction and terminates in the amygdala. As a consequence, a coronal section of brain shows two portions of the caudate nucleus, viz., the more dorsal body and ventral tail. The substantia nigra is located in the midbrain and is divided into two regions: (1) the substantia nigra reticulata (SNr) and (2) the substantia nigra compacta (SNc). The SNr in combination with the globus pallidus acts to inhibit the thalamus. By contrast, the SNc provides the major dopamine projection to the striatum (striatonigral pathway) thus regulating the activity of the striatum as a whole.

Globus Pallidus

The globus pallidus ('pale globe' or 'pallidum') is specifically involved in the regulation of voluntary movement so that actions are carried out 'smoothly'. A large number of myelinated fibres run through the globus pallidus contributing to its pale appearance. It comprises a large structure with a smaller ventral extension ('ventral pallidum'). The anterior and medial border of the globus pallidus are formed by the internal capsule and it is separated from the putamen by the external medullary stria.

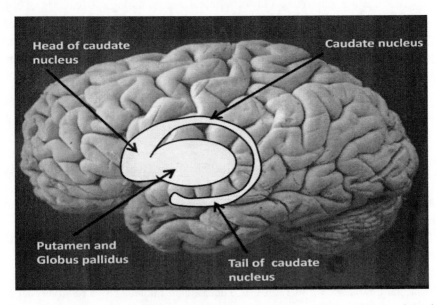

Figure 1. Three-dimensional structure of the basal ganglia superimposed on to a lateral view of the cerebral hemispheres.

Table 1. Clinical diagnostic criteria

Disorder	Abbreviation	Criteria	Reference
Parkinson's disease	PD	Modified UK PD Society Clinical Diagnostic Criteria	Hughes et al. (1992)
Progressive supranuclear palsy	PSP	NINDS-SPSP	Litvan et al. (1996a;b)
Dementia with Lewy bodies	DLB	CDLB	McKeith et al. (1996)
Multiple system atrophy	MSA	Minneapolis Consensus Criteria	Gilman et al. (1998)
Corticobasal degeneration	CBD	NIH office of Rare Disorders	Dickson et al. (2002)

NIH = National Institute of Health, NINDS-SPSP = National Institute of Neurological Disorders and Stroke and the Society of PSP, CDLB = Consortium on Dementia with Lewy bodies) for the parkinsonian syndromes (PD = Parkinson's disease, PSP = progressive supranuclear palsy, DLB = dementia with Lewy bodies, MSA = multiple system atrophy, CBD = corticobasal degeneration.

The caudal region of the globus pallidus is continuous with the rostral part of the SNr and the two regions show a similar ultrastructural organisation (Fox and Rafols, 1976). Its primary action is inhibitory and it therefore balances the excitatory effects of other areas of brain such as the cerebral cortex and cerebellum. The globus pallidus is regarded as a single neural structure but can be divided into two regions separated by the internal medullary stria: (1) the internal (or medial) globus pallidus (GPi) and (2) the external (or lateral) globus pallidus (GPe). The GPe receives input primarily from the striatum and projects to the subthalamic nucleus. By contrast, the GPi receives input from the striatum via the 'direct' and 'indirect' pathways. Electron microscopy suggests clear ultrastructural differences in neurons and synaptic organisation between the globus pallidus and striatum (Pasik et al., 1976). Hence, neurons within the globus pallidus are of the multipolar motor-type and are parvalbumin-immunoreactive with large dendritic arborizations, and occur at low density, while there are relatively few smaller local-circuit neurons. These neurons continually fire in the absence of any input from other areas of brain but signals from the striatum act to pause or reduce the rate of firing.

Functional Circuits of the Basal Ganglia

The major functional circuits of the basal ganglia are shown in Figure 2. In the 'direct' pathway, the cerebral cortex projects an excitatory input to the striatum, which in turn provides an inhibitory input to the SNr and GPi (the SNr-GPi complex). The SNr-GPi complex projects an inhibitory input onto the thalamus which results in a net reduction of the inhibitory effect of the thalamus. Finally, the thalamus projects an excitatory effect to the cerebral cortex, especially the motor cortex, resulting in an overall stimulatory effect. This effect is then transmitted to the brain stem, lateral corticospinal tract, and ultimately to the muscles of the body.

The indirect pathway is more complex. As in the direct pathway, cortical neurons stimulate the striatum which projects an inhibitory input to the GPe which in turn inhibits the subthalamic nucleus, resulting in a net reduction of the inhibitory effect of the subthalamic nucleus.

The subthalamic nucleus provides and excitatory input to the SNr-GPi complex which then inhibits the thalamus thus decreasing the degree of stimulation of the motor cortex resulting ultimately, in reduced muscle activity. As a consequence, the direct and indirect pathways are antagonistic in their control over muscle movement.

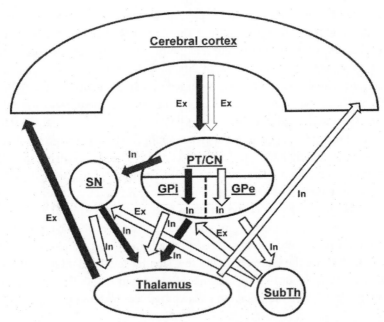

Abbreviations: CN = Caudate nucleus, GPi = Internal globus pallidus, GPe = External globus pallidus, PT = Putamen, SN = Substantia nigra, SubTh = Subthalamic nucleus, Ex = Excitatory projection, In = Inhibitory projection.

Figure 2. Anatomical connections of the basal ganglia: the direct and indirect pathways.

Parkinson's Disease (PD)

PD is common throughout the world although the disorder is less frequent in China, Japan, and in the black population and is the most common parkinsonian disorder (Sagar, 1991).

Clinical Signs and Symptoms

The three most characteristic signs of PD are akinesia, rigidity, and tremor (Walton, 1985). Akinesia describes the 'slowness of movement', the initiation of a movement being especially affected. Rigidity describes an increase in muscle tone which results in stiffness of the limbs and manifest as 'lead-pipe' or 'cog-wheel' rigidity.

Lead-pipe rigidity refers to the general stiffness of a limb which changes little as the arm is moved. In cog-wheel rigidity, the arm 'catches' as it moves, rather as if it were controlled by a cog-wheel.

The patient may also have a 'blank' facial expression and there is loss of blinking and emotional content. Moreover, increased flexion of muscles in the upper back may cause the spine to bend forward leading to a characteristic 'stooped' appearance. Tremor occurs at a frequency of 4-8Hz and primarily affects the fingers, hands, and head.

Tremor is most severe while the limb is at rest but improves as it is used. Tremor is often increased by anxiety and disappears during sleep. In addition, patients treated with *levodopa (L-dopa)* may exhibit 'dyskinesia' or 'dystonia'. In dyskinesia, the patient fidgets, twitches, or is generally restless while dystonia describes a spasm of one set of muscles often deforming a limb into an abnormal posture.

Neuropathology

In PD, the substantia nigra appears to be particularly affected. This region is reduced in size as a result of the death of most of the pigmented neurons. Cells in the substantia nigra (cell group A9 of the SNc) project to the striatum via the striatonigral pathway, a projection which uses dopamine as neurotransmitter.

Hence, there is decreased connectivity between the SNc, globus pallidus, and subthalamic nucleus in PD (Wu et al., 2012). This pathway has an inhibitory influence on the activity of the striatum and the resulting increased activity of these cells may be responsible for the tremor and rigidity characteristic of PD. The surviving neurons of the substantia nigra and cerebral cortex frequently contain 'inclusions' known as Lewy bodies (LB) (Figure 3).

LB are found in the cytoplasm of the cell and may be derived from cytoskeletal filaments. In addition, LB contain significant amounts of the protein α-synuclein (Spillantini et al., 1998). α-Synuclein is a small pre-synaptic protein which ensures the normal functioning of dopamine transporter and tyrosine hydroxylase.

It normally exists in a relatively unfolded state and is highly soluble, but in PD, undergoes a conformational change to insoluble amyloid fibrils that form a major component of the LB.

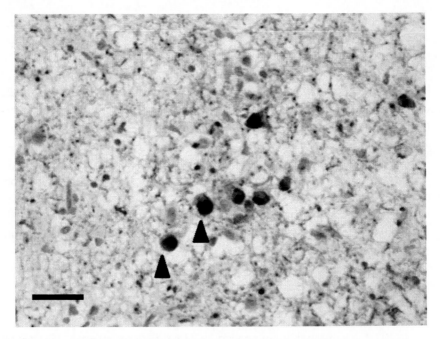

Figure 3. Section through the cerebral cortex showing the presence of Lewy bodies (LB) (arrows) within the neurons. These structures probably represent abnormalities of the neuronal cytoskeleton resulting from degeneration (Section immunolabelled with antibodies against α-synuclein, magnification bar = 50μm).

Progressive Supranuclear Palsy (PSP)

PSP is a rare disorder first described in 1964 and originally called Steele-Richardson-Olszewski syndrome (Steele et al., 1964). The onset of PSP is usually between 60 and 65 years of age and disease duration is usually between five and six years (Nath et al., 2001).

Clinical Signs and Symptoms

PSP patients exhibit supranuclear ophthalmoplegia, pseudobulbar palsy (a bilateral loss of function of the lower cranial nerves causing problems with swallowing and difficulties in speech), and dystonic rigidity (slowness of movement and muscle rigidity affecting the neck and upper trunk) (Steele et al., 1964).

Less consistent clinical signs are dysfunction of the cerebellum and pyramidal motor system together with a relatively mild dementia. PSP, however, is a complex syndrome in which the clinical development vary markedly among patients (Papapetropoulos et al., 2005). The most characteristic symptoms include gait and balance problems, the patient walking clumsily, and often falling backwards. The most obvious visual sign is an inability to direct the gaze of the eyes downwards ('vertical gaze palsy'). There may be changes in personality and loss of interest in the ordinary activities of life. The patient may tire easily, become forgetful, and lose emotional control. As the disease progresses, there is difficulty in controlling movements of the eyes and eyelids. Speech may become slurred and the patient finds it increasingly difficult to swallow solid food or liquid. Tremor of the hands, however, is rare in PSP. A small number of PSP patients develop a more severe dementia associated with the appearance of pathological changes in the cerebral cortex (Gomez-Haro et al., 1999). There may be at least two clinical 'subtypes' of PSP, viz., type 1 (PSP-RS), the commonest subtype, is characterized by postural instability, falls, vertical supranuclear gaze palsy, and cognitive problems while type 2 (PSP-P) is characterized by symptoms largely affecting one side of the body, tremor, and a moderate reaction to the drug *L-dopa*.

Neuropathology

At post-mortem, the brain of a patient with PSP may show only minor abnormalities and is often normal in appearance. Brain weight may be reduced to some extent compared with normal and if brain abnormalities are present these usually involve the midbrain which can appear shrunken and atrophic. When the midbrain is sectioned, the substantia nigra and red nuclei often appear discoloured. In addition, magnetic resonance volumetry and shape analysis suggest that the volume of the right head of the caudate nucleus is lower in PSP (Saini et al., 2013). There is also marked atrophy of the globus pallidus (Cordato et al., 2000) while in the cerebellum, the superior peduncles and the dentate nuclei may be reduced in size and the hillus discoloured.

On histological investigation, several characteristic pathological features are apparent. There is loss of neurons, proliferation of glial cells (gliosis), the presence of abnormal protein aggregates in the cytoplasm of neurons termed neurofibrillary tangles (NFT), the appearance of intracellular vacuoles (granulovacuolar change), and loss of myelin (Lantos, 1994).

The distribution of the pathological features shows a consistent pattern in different patients. Hence, the globus pallidus is nearly always affected in PSP along with the subthalamic nucleus, and substantia nigra (Armstrong et al., 2007). Early stage PSP may exhibit degeneration of the substantia nigra and subthalamic nucleus only suggesting that spread of the disease to affect the globus pallidus occurs later in the process (Sakai and Yamada, 2011).

The appearance of NFT either as 'globose' or 'flame-shaped' cytoplasmic inclusions in specific brain areas is a common pathological feature of PSP. These lesions are not unique to PSP, however, and are found in several disorders, most notably in Alzheimer's disease (AD) (Armstrong, 1993). The most significant molecular constituent of the NFT is the microtubule associated protein (MAP) tau, a protein which is involved in the assembly and stabilization of microtubules, and therefore important in establishing and maintaining neuronal morphology. In normal neurons, tau is soluble and binds reversibly to microtubules with a rapid turnover (Conrad et al., 1992). In disorders such as PSP, however, tau does not bind to the microtubules but collects as insoluble aggregates in the form of paired helical filaments (PHF). The PHF resist proteolysis and ultimately accumulate as NFT resulting in the death of neurons. Hence, aggregation of an abnormal form of tau within cells of the basal ganglia may be a cause of the movement problems of PSP. The NFT are accompanied by neurons that exhibit abnormal swelling of the cell body ('ballooned neurons'), and by the appearance of abnormal 'tufted' astrocytes (Yamada et al., 1992, Ikeda et al., 1995, Komori et al., 1999).

Dementia with Lewy Bodies (DLB)

DLB (also known as 'Lewy body dementia' or 'diffuse Lewy body disease') may account for up to a quarter of all cases of dementia (Lippa et al., 1994; Mckeith et al., 1996). It is characterised by a progressive mental impairment and typical features include fluctuating cognition, visual hallucinations, and parkinsonism.

Clinical Signs and Symptoms

DLB is characterised by a "progressive decline in the mental ability of the patient of sufficient magnitude to interfere with normal social or occupational function" (McKeith et al., 1996).

Prominent and persistent memory impairments may not occur in the early stages, but are evident at some stage of the disease. Problems of attention and in visuo-spatial ability are common, the latter including difficulties in drawing the shapes of common objects. The majority of patients with DLB exhibit at least two of the following features (McKeith et al., 1996): (1) fluctuating cognitive ability with variation in attention and alertness, (2) frequent visual hallucinations that are typically well-formed and detailed, and (3) the motor features characteristic of parkinsonian syndromes (Galasko et al., 1996). Hence, typical PD features include shuffling gait, reduced arm-swinging while walking, blank expression, rigidity, 'ratchet-like' cogwheeling movements, low speech volume, and difficulties in swallowing. There may be two distinct clinical syndromes: (1) DLB with dementia and parkinsonism characterised by prominent hallucinations, and rapid eye movement sleep behavioural disorder, and 2) DLB with 'parkinsonian dementia syndrome' in which the symptoms of parkinsonism predominate (Cummings, 2004).

There are several additional features that support a diagnosis of DLB, viz., repeated falls, syncope (fainting due to a sudden fall in blood pressure), transient loss of consciousness, sensitivity to neuroleptic drugs, delusions, and other types of sensory hallucination (Lauterbach, 2004). Rapid eye movement (REM) sleep behavioural disorder is often regarded as a sign of impending DLB (Turner, 2002). By contrast, features less suggestive of DLB include vascular disease, such as stroke, or the presence of other types of brain disorder which could account for the clinical symptoms. Males may be more susceptible than females and often have a worse prognosis (Kosaka, 1990).

Neuropathology

Brain atrophy in DLB has been described as similar to that in AD (Mann and Snowden, 1995) but in other studies, the size of parietal, frontal, and temporal lobes was reported to be intermediate between those of AD and cognitively normal brain (Robles and Cacabelos, 1999). In the cerebral cortex, areas of the temporal lobe such as the superior temporal gyrus and parahippocampal gyrus are affected, together with regions of the limbic system such as the hippocampus and amygdala. Other cortical regions involved include the cingulate gyrus, insula, claustrum, superior frontal cortex, and occipital cortex. Within the basal ganglia, the putamen and caudate nucleus are affected but the globus pallidus appears to be spared (Jellinger and

Attems, 2006, Perneczky et al., 2007). Cells of the substantia nigra are also likely to exhibit pathological changes.

The essential feature necessary for a neuropathological diagnosis of DLB is the presence of the characteristic LB (Figure 3) (Armstrong, 2008). LB have a different distribution in the brain in DLB compared with PD. In DLB, there are significant numbers of LB in the cerebral cortex whereas in PD, they are largely confined to the substantia nigra.

Significant numbers of LB are also observed in the insula while fewer LB have been recorded in the frontal, parietal, and occipital regions (Harding et al., 2002).

Multiple System Atrophy (MSA)

MSA is a relatively 'new' descriptive term derived from three previously described diseases: (1) olivopontocerebellar atrophy, (2) striato-nigral degeneration, and (3) Shy-Drager syndrome (Probst-Cousin et al., 2000).

Clinical Signs and Symptoms

Approximately 74% of MSA patients exhibit autonomic failure, 87% parkinsonism, 54% cerebellar ataxia, and 49% pyramidal signs such as paralysis, muscle weakness, loss of muscle control, and tremor. The most consistent clinical syndrome in MSA is the presence of parkinsonism, followed by autonomic dysfunction, cerebellar ataxia, and pyramidal tract signs (Wenning et al., 1997).

Of the autonomic system problems, urinary dysfunction is the more common symptom and an earlier manifestation of the disease than postural low blood pressure. Patients with either predominantly cerebellar signs or parkinsonism are regarded as distinct subtypes of MSA and designated as MSA-C and MSA-P respectively. MSA-C patients have marginally increased survival times but the prognosis is poor for most patients. Patients with MSA-P often have abnormal movements of the hands and fingers referred to as a 'jerky' tremor or myoclonus. No abnormal movements are usually present at rest. When holding a posture, however, small amplitude, non-rhythmic movements of one or a few fingers may occur.

There is a moderate intellectual impairment in some patients but severe loss of cognitive function or dementia is unusual (Wenning et al., 1997).

Neuropathology

The cerebral cortex in MSA is usually significantly smaller than in cognitively normal patients, the degree of atrophy reflecting disease duration rather than the age of the patient (Horimoto et al., 2000).

In addition, there may be a specific and progressive cerebral atrophy affecting the frontal lobes (Konogaya et al., 1999) and the motor/premotor areas. In the cerebellum, pathology is more evident in the vermis than the hemispheres and is correlated with disease duration (Tsuchiya et al., 1998). Within the basal ganglia, the substantia nigra is often pale due to loss of pigment.

In addition, there may be atrophy and discolouration of the striatum, specifically affecting the putamen, and this is more evident in the MSA-P subtype (Figure 4). These results are in accord with those of functional brain scans such as PET which suggest widespread hypometabolism of the brain, glucose metabolism being significantly reduced in the cerebellum, brainstem, and striatum.

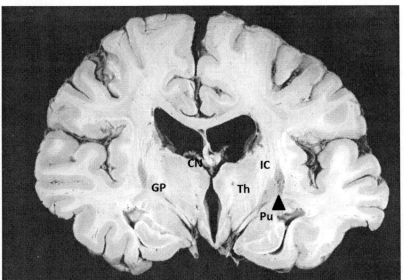

Abbreviations: CN = Caudate nucleus, GP = Globus pallidus, IC = Internal capsule, Pu = Putamen, Th = Thalamus.

Figure 4. Coronal section of the brain of a patient with multiple system atrophy (MSA).

The cellular neuropathology of MSA is characterised by neuronal loss, gliosis, and myelin pathology in selective brain areas including the putamen, caudate nucleus, external pallidum, substantia nigra, locus caeruleus, inferior olive, pontine nuclei, Purkinje cells of the cerebellum, and intermediate cell columns of the spinal cord (Lantos, 1994; Wenning et al., 1997). The most characteristic pathological change is the presence of abnormal protein aggregates, termed glial cytoplasmic inclusions (GCI), which are found mainly in oligodendrocytes and first described in 1989 (Papp et al., 1989). This pathology often affects the substantia nigra, striatum, inferior olivary nucleus, pontine nuclei, and cerebellum (Dickson et al., 1999). The GCI comprise abnormal aggregations of silver-positive, 10-15nm diameter coated filaments, the major molecular constituent of which is the protein α-synuclein. Pathological inclusions have also been observed in the nuclei, cytoplasm, and cell processes of neurons in MSA (Dickson et al., 1999). In addition, morphological abnormalities of neurons can be observed including enlargement or atrophy of the cell body (Armstrong et al., 2004).

Corticobasal Degeneration (CBD)

CBD is a rare, progressive movement based on a study of three original cases initially described as 'corticodentatonigral degeneration achromasia" (Rebeiz et al., 1968). Subsequently, various names have been applied to the disorder including 'corticoganglionic degeneration' (CBGD), but CBD remains the most popular descriptive term.

Clinical Signs and Symptoms

The onset of CBD is usually after 60 years of age, death following within eight years after disease onset. The clinical diagnosis of CBD is difficult as symptoms often resemble those of other types of disorder. The most characteristic clinical features are limb dysfunction (Rinne et al., 1994; Schneider et al,. 1997), parkinsonism (Ueno, 1996), apraxia (Schneider et al., 1997), and dementia (Ueno, 1996).

The onset of the disease is relatively sudden (Wadia and Lang, 2007), patients exhibiting problems related to cortical processing and motor dysfunction. The major clinical features include cortical signs, parkinsonism, palsy, myoclonus, and dementia (Ueno, 1996).

The most common initial symptom is asymmetric limb clumsiness with or without accompanying rigidity or tremor (Rinne et al., 1994; Wenning et al., 1998). Subsequently, the disease progresses to affect gait with a slow progression to affect the ipsilateral arms and legs (Rinne et al., 1994). Apraxia and cortical dementia are the most common cortical signs (Wenning et al., 1998).

The motor symptoms of CBD include parkinsonism, 'alien hand syndrome', and apraxia. Parkinsonism usually affects the extremities of a limb, is frequently asymmetric, and characterised by rigidity and bradykinesia. 'Alien hand syndrome' is present in approximately 60% of patients and is a failure to control movements of the hand accompanied by a sensation that the hand is 'foreign' to the patient. The affected hand may also try to 'avoid' specific external stimuli such as heat, cold, or touch and may exhibit an itching or prickling sensation. By contrast, apraxia is characterized by an inability to repeat a specific movement of the hands and arms or an inability to carry out such a movement on command. 'Limb-kinetic' apraxia may also occur and is a dysfunction of fine movement control involving the hands (Belfor et al., 2006). Myoclonus has been observed in CBD and may be the result from dysfunction of an enhanced 'long-loop reflex pathway', a different pathway from that involved in classic 'cortical reflex' myoclonus (Carella et al., 1997).

Neuropathology

Neuropathologically, CBD is characterised by a progressive and asymmetric cortical atrophy affecting the anterior cerebral cortex (Tsuchiya et al., 1997), the fronto-parietal region (Ikeda, 1997), and the superior temporal cortex (Ikeda, 1997). As a consequence, the disease is often regarded as a pathological subtype of frontotemporal dementia (FTD) (Cairns et al., 2007), the second most frequent form of cortical dementia of early-onset after AD. There is atrophy of the basal ganglia, including the caudate nucleus (Markus et al., 1995) and substantia nigra (Kawasaki et al., 1996) and mild to moderate gliosis and neuronal loss in the putamen, globus pallidus and subthalamic nucleus (Rippon et al., 2005). The typical gross brain features of a case of CBD often include enlarged lateral ventricles and atrophy of the head of the caudate nucleus, while the internal capsule, insula, putamen, and globus pallidus are more normal in appearance. There is a widespread neuronal and glial pathology in CBD suggesting a generalized cytoskeletal dysfunction affecting several different types of cell (Feany and Dickson, 1995).

These include the presence of EN (Mori and Oda, 1997), neuropil threads (NT) (Komori et al., 1997), NFT (Ikeda, 1997), and glial pathology. The glial pathology includes oligodendroglial inclusions (GI) (Matsumoto et al., 1996) and astrocytic plaques (AP) especially in the caudate nucleus (Dickson et al., 1996). These lesions are particularly severe in the posterior frontal area anterior to the precentral gyrus but are less severe in the primary motor area (Tsuchiya et al., 1997). The EN of CBD are present in various regions including the frontal cortex (Halliday et al., 1995), cingulate gyrus (CG), SFG, motor cortex, brainstem tegmentum, basal ganglia, thalamus, insula, claustrum, and amygdala (Matsumoto et al., 1996, Holliday et al., 1995).

Differential Pathology in the Basal Ganglia

Many of the same anatomical pathways involving the globus pallidus are likely to be affected in all parkinsonian syndromes leading to considerable overlap in clinical symptoms. However, there may also be variations in the severity to which different regions of the basal ganglia are affected leading to possible differences in clinical symptoms (Table 2). For example, significant atrophy of the putamen is likely to lead to gait ataxia while increasing pathology in the caudate nucleus may lead to early falls and supranuclear gaze palsy (Song et al., 2011).

The SNc produces the neurotransmitter dopamine and provides the major dopamine projection to the striatum via the striatonigral pathway, the function of which is to regulate the activity of the striatum as a whole. In particular, the antagonistic functions of the direct and indirect pathways are influenced by the activity of the SNc. This pathway is commonly affected in all parkinsonian syndromes (Song et al., 2011), although most significantly in PD itself (Kusbeci et al., 2012). First, in the presence of dopamine, D1-receptors in the basal ganglia stimulate inhibitory neurons which favour the direct pathway. Second, inhibitory neurons of the indirect pathway are stimulated primarily by the excitatory neurotransmitters acetylcholine and glutamate. This results in an inhibition of the motor cortex and as a consequence, less movement. In the presence of dopamine, the basal ganglia D2-receptors inhibit the inhibitory neurons thus reducing the effect of the indirect inhibitory pathway. Hence, the overall effect is that the striatonigral pathway increases the excitatory effect of the direct pathway and reduces the inhibitory effect of the indirect pathway.

As a consequence, in PD and the other disorders, the loss of dopamine causes a reduction in the function of the direct pathway resulting in poor initiation of movement while over-activity of the indirect pathway causes inhibition of movement. These changes are likely to be a major cause of the characteristic movement disorders of PD and related disorders, viz., akinesia, rigidity, and tremor (Walton, 1985).

The degree to which other regions of the basal ganglia are affected, however, may vary considerably between patients with parkinsonism. Hence, in a magnetic resonance (MR) study of the basal ganglia in five patients with 'parkinsonian syndrome' (da Costa et al., 2003), a bilateral hypersignal was observed in the substantia nigra exclusively in three patients, exclusively in the globus pallidus in one patient, and in substantia nigra, globus pallidus, and affecting the striatonigral pathway in one patient.

In addition, there may be differences between PSP subtypes, atrophy of the GPi being more severe in the PSP-RS subtype (Schofield et al., 2011).

Moreover, in a positron emission tomography (PET) study of dopamine transporter loss, there was a greater and earlier loss of dopamine transporter in the anterior caudate and ventral putamen in PSP and MSA compared with PD (Oh et al., 2012).

Table 2. Summary of differential pathology affecting the globus pallidus and other areas of the basal ganglia in the parkinsonian syndromes

	Region of the basal ganglia				
Syndrome	Globus pallidus	Caudate nucleus	Putamen	Substantia nigra	Subthalamic nucleus
PD	Less affected	Less affected	Less affected	Significantly affected	Less affected
PSP	Markedly affected	Affected (head?)	Significantly affected (early)	Affected (early)	Affected (early)
DLB	Spared	Affected	Affected	Affected	?
MSA	Affected	Affected	Significantly affected (early)	Affected	?
CBD	Mild to mod. affected	Significantly affected	Mild to mod. affected	Affected	Mild to mod. affected

PD = Parkinson's disease, PSP = progressive supranuclear palsy, DLB = dementia with Lewy bodies, MSA = multiple system atrophy, CBD = corticobasal degeneration, mod. = moderately affected, ? no detailed pathological studies.

Hence, gait ataxia, early falls and supranuclear gaze palsy are more likely to be present in PSP and MSA than in PD. Further evidence for more severe pathology in the putamen in PSP comes from a study of the changes in the MR relaxation properties (Foroutan et al., 2013). The globus pallidus and substantia nigra contain large amounts of iron which can be measured using MR. Hence, the iron burden is increased in the basal ganglia in PSP, but only significantly in the putamen. By contrast, in the study of Han et al. (2013), pathological iron burden was greater in the substantia nigra and globus pallidus in PSP and in the putamen in MSA. In addition, MR spectroscopy measuring brain tissue metabolites such as N-acetylaspartate in the globus pallidus and putamen have found lower levels in MSA-P and PSP compared with controls and lower in the putamen of PSP compared with MSA-P (Guevera et al., 2010) which may explain the greater frequency of vertical gaze palsy in PSP. The basal ganglia are also affected in DLB, including the putamen and caudate nucleus, but the globus pallidus appears to be spared (Jellinger and Attems, 2006, Perneczky et al., 2007). In addition, in CBD there is atrophy of the caudate nucleus but the putamen and globus pallidus are generally spared. These differences are also likely to lead to differences in clinical symptoms. Hence, gait ataxia, in combination with early falls and supranuclear gaze palsy, is more likely in DLB while uncomplicated gait ataxia is more likely in CBD.

Conclusion

The globus pallidus, together with the striatum, substantia nigra, nucleus accumbens, and subthalamic nucleus constitute the basal ganglia, a group on nuclei which act as a single functional unit. The action of the globus pallidus is primarily inhibitory and balances the excitatory influence of other areas of the brain such as the cerebral cortex and cerebellum. Neuropathological changes affecting the basal ganglia play a significant role in the clinical signs and symptoms observed in the 'parkinsonian syndromes' viz., Parkinson's disease (PD), progressive supranuclear palsy (PSP), dementia with Lewy bodies (DLB), multiple system atrophy (MSA), and corticobasal degeneration. There is increasing evidence that areas of the basal ganglia are differentially affected in these disorders. Hence, differential pathology affecting the functional pathways of the basal ganglia, including the globus pallidus, is likely to contribute to similarities and difference in movement in the parkinsonian syndromes.

References

Armstrong, R. A. Is the clustering of neurofibrillary tangles in Alzheimer's patients related to the cells of origin of specific cortico-cortical projections? *Neuroscience Letters* 1993, 160, 57-60.

Armstrong, R. A. Visual signs and symptoms of Parkinson's disease. *Clinical and Experimental Optometry* 2008, 91, 129-138.

Armstrong, R. A. Visual signs and symptoms of progressive supranuclear palsy. *Clinical and Experimental Optometry* 2011, 95,150-160.

Armstrong, R. A. Visual signs and symptoms of dementia with Lewy bodies. *Clinical and Experimental Optometry* 2012, 94, 621-630.

Armstrong, R. A., Cairns, N. J., Lantos, P. L. The spatial patterns of Lewy bodies, senile plaques and neurofibrillary tangles in dementia with Lewy bodies. *Experimental Neurology* 1998, 150, 122-127.

Armstrong, R. A., Cairns, N. J., Lantos, P. L. A quantitative study of the pathological lesions in the neocortex and hippocampus of 12 patients with corticobasal degeneration. *Experimental Neurology* 2000, 163, 348-356.

Armstrong, R. A., Cairns, N. J., Lantos, P. L. A quantitative study of the pathological changes in ten patients with multiple system atrophy (MSA). *Journal of Neural Transmission* 2004, 111, 485-495.

Armstrong, R. A., Lantos, P. L., Cairns, N. J. Progressive supranuclear palsy (PSP): a quantitative study of the pathological changes in cortical and subcortical areas of eight cases. *Journal of Neural Transmission* 2007, 114, 1569-1577.

Armstrong, R. A., Cairns, N. J. Clustering and spatial correlations of the neuronal cytoplasmic inclusions, astrocytic plaques, and ballooned neurons in corticobasal degeneration. *Journal of Neural Transmission* 2009, 116, 1103-1110.

Belfor, N., Amici, S., Boxer, A. L., Kramer, J. H., Gorno-Tempini, M. L., Rosen, H. J., Miller, B. L. Clinical and neuropsychological; features of corticobasal degeneration. *Mechanisms of Aging and Development* 2006, 127, 203 -207.

Brodal, A. (1981) *Neurological anatomy: in relation to clinical medicine.* 3rd Ed., Oxford University Press, London and New York.

Cairns, N. J., Bigio, E. H., Mackenzie, I. R. A., Neumann, M., Lee, V. M. Y., Hatanpaa, K. J., White, C. L., Schneider, J. A., Halliday, G., Duyckaertes, C., Lowe, J. S., Holm, I. E., Tolnay, M., Okamoto, K., Yokoo, H., Murayama, S., Woulfe, J., Munoz, D. G., Dickson, D. W., Ince, P. G., Trojanowski, J. Q., Mann, D. M. A. Neuropathologic diagnostic and nosological criteria for frontotemporal lobar degeneration: consensus of the Consortium for Frontotemporal Lobar Degeneration. *Acta Neuropathologica* 2007, 114, 5-22.

Carella, F., Ciano, C., Panzica, F., Scaioli, V. Myoclonus in corticobasal degeneration. *Movement Disorders* 1997, 12, 598-603.

Conrad, C., Andreadis, A., Trojanowski, J. Q., Dickson, D. W., Kang, D., Chen, X. H., Wiederholt, W., Hansen, L., Masliah, E., Thal, L. J., Katzman, R., Xia, Y., Saitoh, T. Genetic evidence for the involvement of tau in progressive supranuclear palsy. *Annals of Neurology* 1997, 41, 277-281.

Cordata, N. J., Halliday, G. M., Harding, A. J., Hely, M. A., Morris, J. G. L. Regional brain atrophy in progressive supranuclear palsy and Lewy body disease. *Annals of Neurology* 2000, 47, 718-728.

Cummings, J. L. Dementia with Lewy bodies: Molecular pathogenesis and implications for classification. *Journal of Geriatric Psychology and Neurology* 2004, 17, 112-119.

Da Costa, M. D. L., Goncalves, L. R., Barbosa, E. R., Bacheschi, L. A. Neuroimaging abnormalities in parkinconism: study of five cases. *Arquivos de Neuro-Psiquiatria* 2003, 61, 381-386.

Dickson, D. W., Feany, M. B., Yen, S. H., Mattiace, L. A., and Davies, P. Cytoskeletal pathology in non-Alzheimer degenerative dementia: new lesions in diffuse Lewy body disease, Pick's disease and corticobasal degeneration. *Journal of Neural Transmission* 47, 31-46.

Dickson, D. W., Bergeron, C., Chin, S. S., Duyckaerts, C., Horoupian, D., Ikeda, K., Jellinger, K., Lantos, P. L., Lippa, C. F., Mirra, S. S., Tabaton, M., Vonsattel, J. P., Wakabayashi, K., Litvan, I. Office of rare diseases neuropathologic criteria for corticobasal degeneration. *Journal of Neuropathology and Experimental Neurology* 2002, 61, 935-946.

Dickson, D. W., Liu, W. L., Liu, W. K., Yen, S. H. Multiple system atrophy: a sporadic synucleinopathy. *Brain Pathology,* 1999, 9, 721-732.

Feany, M. B., Dickson, D. W. Widespread cytoskeletal pathology characterises corticobasal degeneration. *American Journal of Pathology* 1995, 146, 1388-1396.

Foroutan, P., Murray, M. E., Fujioka, S., Schweitzer, K. J., Dickson, D. W., Wszolek, Z. K., Grant, S. C. Progressive supranuclear palsy: High-field-strength MR microscopy in the human substantia nigra and globus pallidus. *Radiology* 2013, 266, 280-288.

Fox, C. A., Rafols, J. A. The striatal efferents in the globus pallidus and the substantia nigra. In: *The Basal ganglia* (MD Yahr, ed.), Raven press, New York, 1976, 37-55,

Galasko, D., Katzman, R., Salmon, D. P., Hansen, I. Clinical and neuropathological findings in Lewy body dementias. *Brain and Cognition* 1996, 31, 166-175.

Gilman, S., Low, P. A., Quinn, N., Albanese, A., Ben-Schlomo, Y., Fowler, C. J., Kaufmann, H., Klockgether, T., Lang, A. E., Lantos, P. L., Litvan, I., Mathias, C. J., Oliver, E., Robertson, D., Schatz, I., Wenning, G. K. Consensus statement on the diagnosis of multiple system atrophy. *Journal of Autonomic Nervous System* 1998, 74, 189-192.

Gomez-Haro, C., Espert-Tortajada, R., Gadea-Domenech, M., Navarro-Humanes, J. F. Progressive supranuclear palsy: Neurological, neuropathological and neuropsychological aspects. *Revue de Neurologie* 1999, 29, 936-956.

Guevara, C. A., Blain, C. R., Stahl, D., Lythgoe, D. J., Leigh, P. N., Barker, G. J. Quantitative magnetic resonance spectroscopic imaging in Parkinson's disease, progressive supranuclear palsy, and multiple system atrophy. *European Journal of Neurology* 2010, 17, 1193-1202.

Han, Y. H., Lee, J. H., Kang, B. M., Mun, C. W., Baik, S. K., Shin, Y., Park, K. H. Topographical differences of brain iron deposition between progressive supranuclear palsy and parkinsonian variant multiple system atrophy. *Journal of Neurological Sciences* 2013, 325, 29-35.

Harding, A. J., Broe, G. A., Halliday, G. M. Visual hallucinations in Lewy body disease relate to Lewy bodies in the temporal lobe. *Brain* 2002, 125, 391-403.

Halliday, G. M., Davies, L., Mcritchie, D. A., Cartwright, H., Pamphlett, R., Morris, J. G. L. Ubiquitin positive lesions in corticobasal degeneration. *Acta Neuropathologica* 1995, 90, 68-75.

Horimoto, Y., Aiba, I., Yasuda, T., Ohkawa, Y., Katayama, T., Yokokawa, Y., Goto, A., Ito, Y. Cerebral atrophy in multiple system atrophy by MRI. *Journal of Neurological Science* 2000, 173, 109-112.

Hughes, A. J., Daniel, S. E., Kilford, L., Lees, A. J. Accuracy of clinical diagnosis of idiopathic Parkinson disease: a clinic-pathological study of 100 cases. *Journal of Neurology, Neurosurgery and Pyschiatry* 1992, 55, 181-184

Ikeda, K. Basic pathology of corticobasal degeneration. *Neuropathology* 1997, 17, 127-133.

Ikeda, K., Akiyama, H., Kondo, H., Haga, C., Tanno, E., Tokuda, T., Ikeda, S. Thorn-shaped astrocytes: possibly secondarily induced tau-positive glial fibrillary tangles. *Acta Neuropathologica* 1995, 90, 620-625.

Jellinger, K. A., Attems, J. Does striatal pathology distinguish Parkinson's disease with dementia from dementia with Lewy bodies? *Acta Neuropathologica* 2006, 112, 253-260.

Kawasaki, K., Iwanaga, K., Wakabayashi, K., Yamada, M., Nagai, H., Idezuka, J., Homna, Y., Ikuta, F. Corticobasal degeneration with neither argyrophilic inclusions nor tau abnormalities: a new subgroup. *Acta Neuropathologica* 1996, 91, 140-144.

Komori, T. Tau positive glial inclusions in progressive supranuclear palsy, corticobasal degeneration and Pick's disease. *Brain Pathology* 1999, 9, 663-679.

Komori, T., Arai, N., Oda, M., Nakayama, H., Murayama, S., Amano, N., Shibata, N., Kobayashi, M., Sasaki, S., Yagishita, S. Morphologic differences in neuropil threads in Alzheimer's disease, corticobasal degeneration and progressive supranuclear palsy: a morphometric study. *Neuroscience Letters* 1997, 233, 89-92.

Konogaya, M., Sakai, M., Matsuoka, Y. Konogaya Y, Hashzume Y. Multiple system atrophy with remarkable frontal lobe atrophy. *Acta Neuropathologica* 1999, 97, 423-428.

Kosaka, K. Diffuse Lewy body disease in Japan. *Journal of Neurology* 1990, 237, 197-204.

Kusbeci, O. Y., Mas, N. G., Yucel, A., Karabekir, H. S., Yazici, A. C. Stereological evaluation of basal ganglia in Parkinson's disease. *Journal of Neurological Sciences-Turkish* 2012, 29, 232-242.

Lantos, P. L. Cellular pathology of multiple system atrophy: a review. *Journal of Neurology, Neurosurgery and Psychiatry* 1994, 57, 129-13.

Lauterbach, E. C. The neuropsychiatry of Parkinson's disease and related disorders. *Psych. Clin. N A* 2004, 27, 801-825.

Lippa, C. F., Smith, T. W., Swearer, J. M. Alzheimer's disease and Lewy body disease: A comparative clinicopathological study. *Annals of Neurology* 1994, 35, 81-88.

Litvan, I., Agid, Y., Calne, D., Campbell, G., Dubois, B., Davoisen, R. C., Goetz, C. G., Golbe, L. I., Grafman, J., Growden, J. H., Hallett, M., Jankovic, J., Quinn, N. P., Tolisa, E., Zee, D. S., Chase, T. W., FitzGibbon, E. J., Hall, Z., Juncos, J., Nelson, K. B., Oliver, E.,

Pramstaller, P., Reich, S. G., Verny, M. Clinical research criteria for the diagnosis of progressive supranuclear palsy (Steele-Richardson-Olszewski syndrome): report of the NINDS-SPSP International Workshop. *Neurology* 1996a, 47, 1-9.

Litvan, I., Hauw, J. J., Bartko, J. J., Lantos, P. L., Daniel, S. E., Horoupian, D. S., McKee, A., Dickson, D., Bancher, C., Tabaton, M., Jellinger, K., Anderson, D. W. Validity and reliability of the preliminary NINDS neuropathological criteria for progressive supranuclear palsy and related disorders. *Journal of Neuropathology and Experimental Neurology* 1996b, 55, 97-105.

Mann, D. M., Snowden, J. S. The topographic distribution of brain atrophy in cortical Lewy body Disease: comparison with Alzheimer's disease. *Acta Neuropathologica* 1995, 89, 178-183.

Markus, H. S., Lees, A. J., Lennox, G., Marsden, C. D., Costa, D. C. Patterns of regional cerebral blood flow in corticobasal degeneration studied using HMPAO SPECT: Comparison with Parkinson's disease and normal controls. *Movement Disorders* 1995, 10, 179-187.

Matsumoto, S., Udaka, F., Kameyama, M., Kusaka, H., Itoh, H., Imai, T. Subcortical neurofibrillary tangles, neuropil threads and argentophilic glial inclusions in corticobasal degeneration. *Clinical Neuropathology* 1996, 15, 209-214.

McKeith, I. G., Galasko, D., Kosaka, K., Perry, E. K., Dickson, D. W., Hansen, L. A., Salmon, D. P., Lowe, J., Mirra, S. S., Byrne, E. J., Lennox, G., Quinn, N. P., Edwardosn, J. A., Ince, P. G., Bergeron, C., Burns, A., Miller, B. L., Lovestone, S., Collerton, D., Jansen, E. N. H., Ballard, C., de Vos, R. A. I., Wilcock, G. K., Jellinger, K. A., Perry, R. H. Consensus guidelines for the clinical and pathological diagnosis of dementia with Lewy bodies (DLB): Report of the consortium on DLB international workshop. *Neurology* 1996, 47, 1113-1124.

Mori, H., Oda, M. Ballooned neurons in corticobasal degeneration and progressive supranuclear palsy. *Neuropathology* 1997, 7, 248-252.

Nath, U., Ben-Shlomo, Y., Thomson, R. G., Morris, H. R., Wood, N. W., Lees, A. J., Burn, D. J. The prevalence of progressive supranuclear palsy (Steele-Richardson-Olszewski syndrome) in the UK. *Brain* 2001, 124, 1438-1449.

Oh, M., Kim, J. S., Kim, J. Y., Shin, K. H., Park, S. H., Kim, H. O., Moon, D. H., Oh, S. J., Chung, S. J., Lee, C. S. Subregional patterns of preferential striatal dopamine transporter loss differ in Parkinson's disease, progressive supranuclear palsy, and multiple system atrophy. *Journal of Nuclear Medicine* 2012, 53, 399-406.

Papapetropoulos, S., Gonzalez, J., Mash, D. C. Natural history of progressive supranuclear palsy: a clinicopathologic study from a population of brain donors. *European Neurology* 2005, 54, 1-9.

Papp, M. I., Kahn, J. E., Lantos, P. L. Glial cytoplasmic inclusions in the CNS of patients with multiple system atrophy (striatonigral degeneration, olivopontocerebellar atrophy, and Shy-Drager syndrome). *Journal of Neurological Science* 1989, 94, 79-100.

Pasik, P., Pasik, T., DiFiglia, M. Quantitative aspects of neuronal organisation in the neostriatum of the macaque monkey. In: *The Basal ganglia* (MD Yahr, ed.), Raven press, New York, 1976, 57-89.

Perneczky, R., Haussermann, P., Diehl-Schmid, J., Boecker, H., Forstl, H., Drzezga, A., Kurz, A. Metabolic correlates of brain reserve power in dementia with Lewy bodies: An FDG PET study. *Dementia and Geriatric Cognitive Disorders* 2007, 23, 416-422.

Probst-Cousin, S., Kayser, C., Heuss, D., Neundorfer, B. Thirty years of multiple system atrophy concept: Review and survey of multiple system atrophy. *Fortschritte Neurol. Psych.* 2000, 68, 25-36.

Rebeiz, J. J., Kolodny, E. H., Richardson, E. P. Corticodentaonigral degeneration with neuronal achromasia. *Archives of Neurology* 1968, 18, 20-33.

Rinne, J. O., Lee, M. S., Thompson, P. D., Marsden, C. D. Corticobasal degeneration: a clinical study of 36 cases. *Brain* 1994, 117, 1183-1196.

Rippon, G. A., Staugaitis, S. M., Chin, S. S. M., Goldman, J. E., Marder, K. Corticobasal sybdrome with novel argyrophilic glial inclusions. *Movement Disorders* 2005, 20, 598-602.

Robles, A., Cacabelos, P. Dementia with Lewy Bodies: New data for the understanding of neuroimaging. *Revue de Neurologie* 1999, 29, 993-998.

Saini, J., Bagepally, B. S., Sandhya, M., Pasha, S. A., Yadav, R., Thennarasu, K., Pal, P. K. Subcortical structures in progressive supranuclear palsy: vertex-based analysis. *European Journal of Neurology* 2013, 20, 493-501.

Sagar, H. *Parkinson's disease.* Optima Health Guides. Macdonald and Co., London, 1991.

Sakai, K., Yamada, M. Early-stage supranuclear palsy with degenerative lesions confined to the subthalamic nucleus and substantia nigra. *Neuropathology* 2011, 31, 77-81.

Schneider, J. A., Watts, R. L., Gearing, M., Brewer, R. P., Mirra, S. S. Corticobasal degeneration: Neuropathological and clinical heterogeneity. *Neurology* 1997, 48, 959-969.

Schofield, E. C., Hodges, J. R., Macdonald, V., Cordata, N. J., Krill, J. J., Halliday, G. M. Cortical atrophy differentiates Richardson's syndrome from the Parkinsonian form of progressive supranuclear palsy. *Movement Disorders* 2011, 26, 256-263.

Song, Y. J. C., Huang, Y., Halliday, G. M. Clinical correlates of similar pathologies in parkinsonian syndromes. *Movement disorders* 2011, 26: 499-506.

Spillantini, M. G., Crowther, R. A., Jakes, R., Cairns, N. J., Lantos, P. L., Goedert, M. Filamentous α-synuclein inclusions link multiple system atrophy with Parkinson's disease and dementia with Lewy bodies. *Neuroscience Letters* 1998, 251, 205-208.

Steele, J. C., Richardson, J. C., Olszewski, T. Progressive supranuclear palsy. *Archives of Neurology* 1964, 10, 333-359.

Tsuchiya, K., Ikeda, K., Uchihara, T., Oda, T., Shimada, H. Distribution of cerebral cortical lesions in corticobasal degeneration: a clinicopathological study of five autopsy cases in Japan. *Acta Neuropathologica* 1997, 94, 416-424.

Tsuchiya, K., Watabiki, S., Sano, M., Iobe, H., Shiotsu, H., Taki, K., Hashimoto, K. Distribution of cerebellar cortical lesions in multiple system atrophy: a topographic neuropathological study of three autopsy cases in Japan. *Journal of Neurological Science* 1998, 155, 80-85.

Turner, R. S. Idiopathic rapid eye movement sleep behavioural disorder is a harbinger of dementia with Lewy bodies. *Journal of Geriatric Psychology and Neurology* 2002, 15, 195-199.

Ueno, E. Clinical features of corticobasal degeneration. *Neuropathology* 1996, 16, 253-256.

Wadia, P. M., Lang, A. E. The many faces of corticobasal degeneration. *Parkinson's Disease and Related Disorders* 2007, 13, S336 – S340.

Walton Sir, J. *Brain's Diseases of the Nervous System.* pp 322-336, Oxford University Press, Oxford, 1985.

Wenning, G. K., Tison, F., Ben-Shlomo, Y., Daniel, S. E., Quinn, N. P. Multiple system atrophy: a review of 203 pathologically proven cases. *Movement Disorders* 1997, 12, 133-147.

Wenning, G. K., Litvan, I., Jankovic, J., Granata, R., Mangone, C. A., McKee, A., Poewe, W., Jellinger, K., Chandhuri, K. R., Dolhaberriague, L., Pearce, R. K. B. Natural history and survival of 14 patients with corticobasal degeneration confirmed at postmortem examination. *Journal of Neurology, Neurosurgery and Psychiatry* 1998, 64, 184-189.

Wu, T., Wang, J., Wang, C. D., Hallett, M., Zang, Y. F., Wu, X. L., Chan, P. Basal ganglia circuits changes in Parkinson's disease. *Neuroscience Letters* 2012, 524, 55-59.

Yamada, T., McGeer, P. L., McGeer, E. G. Appearance of paired nucleated tau-positive glia in patients with progressive supranuclear palsy brain tissue. *Neuroscience Letters* 1992, 135, 99-102.

Index

E

G

H

F

N

O

T

tremor, 62, 94, 98, 99, 101, 104, 107, 109
trial, 31, 35, 71, 72, 76, 77, 80, 81, 84, 89
triggers, 71
turnover, 102
tyrosine, 99
tyrosine hydroxylase, 99

U

UK, 93, 96, 115
United, 57
United States, 57
urinary dysfunction, 104
USA, viii, 2, 5, 6, 11, 26, 31

V

variations, 108

varieties, 3, 4, 79
ventricle, 41, 42
visualization, 36
Volunteers, 5, 18, 19

W

walking, 101, 103
water, 70, 71, 72
weakness, 104
white matter, 4, 5, 7, 8, 9, 13, 19, 20, 26, 27, 36, 41

Y

yield, 81, 87